ELSEVIER MONOGRAPHS

GEO-SCIENCES SECTION

Subseries: Geology

ELSEVIER PUBLISHING COMPANY

AMSTERDAM - NEW YORK

THE GEOLOGICAL ASPECTS
OF THE ORIGIN OF LIFE
ON EARTH

by

M. G. RUTTEN

Professor of Geology
State University, Utrecht
(The Netherlands)

ELSEVIER PUBLISHING COMPANY

AMSTERDAM - NEW YORK

1962

SOLE DISTRIBUTORS FOR THE UNITED STATES AND CANADA
AMERICAN ELSEVIER PUBLISHING COMPANY, INC.
52 Vanderbilt Avenue, New York 17, N.Y.

Library of Congress Catalog Card Number 62-10363

With 36 illustrations and 6 tables

PRINTED IN THE NETHERLANDS BY
CENTRALE DRUKKERIJ, NIJMEGEN

CONTENTS

Chapter I. INTRODUCTION 1
  Interest in the origin of life on earth 1
  Geologists and the origin of life 2
  The biological approach 4
  Religion and the origin of life 5
  About this book 5
  Acknowledgments 6

Chapter II. UNIFORMITARIANISM AND ACTUALISM 7
  Philosophizing about uniformitarianism and actualism . . 7
  Catastrophism and uniformitarianism 9
  Time in geology 10
  Time through a geologist's eye 11
  Variations in intensity of processes: the pulse of the earth . 12
  Schematization in geologic writing 13
  Smaller catastrophes and uniformitarianism 14
  Uniformitarianism and its implications for the origin of life 19

Chapter III. MEASURING TIME IN GEOLOGY 21
  Relative and absolute dating 21
  Relative dating 22
    Principle of superposition, 22 — Organic evolution, 23
    — Eras of relative age in geology, 23 — Relative age
    of sediments and igneous rocks, 24
  Absolute dating 25
    Physical clocks: radioactive decay series, 25 — Con-
    stancy of radioactive decay, 26 — Pleochroitic rings, 26
    — Absolute age of igneous rocks and sediments, 29 —
    Radioactive decay series in geology, 30 — Isotopes, 31
    — Mass spectrometry, 33 — Isotope dilution, 36 —
    Reliability of absolute dating, 37
  The long early history of the earth 39

Chapter IV. THE BIOLOGICAL APPROACH 42
  Moscow symposium of the International Union of
  Biochemistry 42

Non-living and living in biology 42
Non-living and living in geology 44
Chemical uniformity of present mode of life 45
Impossibility of natural synthesis of organic compounds in
the atmosphere 46
The oxygenic atmosphere of the present 47
Anoxygenic primeval atmosphere 48
Inorganic synthesis of 'organic' compounds in primeval
atmosphere 48
Generatio spontanea 50
Experimental checks 51
Chemical diversity of early 'life': the Pirie drawing . . . 57
Mutants acquiring a new skill: organic photosynthesis . 59
Gradual transition from primeval to present atmosphere . 60
The astronomer's view 61

Chapter V. THE TWO ATMOSPHERES: ANOXYGENIC AND OXYGENIC,
PRE-ACTUALISTIC AND ACTUALISTIC 62
Aerobic and anaerobic, oxygenic and anoxygenic . . . 62
Aradiatic for shorter ultraviolet light 63
Pre-actualistic and actualistic 63
Exogenic and endogenic processes 64
Actualism in early exogenic and endogenic processes . . 65

Chapter VI. WHERE TO LOOK FOR REMAINS OF EARLY LIFE: THE
OLD SHIELDS 67
Paucity of early records 67
The old shields 70
Stability of old shields 72
Complex structure of old shields 73

Chapter VII. THE FOSSILS 75
Late pre-Cambrian faunae 75
The importance of microbes 75
Early pre-Cambrian remains 76
The oldest biogenic deposits 77
Anoxygenic metabolism of earliest known organisms . . 82
Structures in biogenic and inorganic limestone deposits . 82
The oldest real fossils 83
Primitive plants from Ontario 85

Reefs of algal limestone in the Sahara 89
Optimistic outlook 92
Chapter VIII. THE ENVIRONMENT 94
Weathering of rocks 94
Minerals unstable in present weathering 95
Minerals stable under anoxygenic atmosphere 96
Studies by Rankama: detritus of granites 97
Studies by Ramdohr: gold-uranium reefs 98
Sands with pyrites, pitchblende and other minerals . . . 99
Age of sediments formed under anoxygenic atmosphere . 109
Studies by Lepp and Goldich: iron formations 109
Sediments formed under oxygenic atmosphere: the red beds 111
Provisional dating of transition between the two atmospheres 113
Type of geological evidence drawn from fossils and from
the environment 114
Chapter IX. MISCELLANEOUS GEOLOGICAL CONSIDERATIONS . . 115
General 115
The importance of clays 116
The importance of quartz 117
Geochemical inventories 118
Uniformity of surface temperature of the earth 120
Glasshouse effect of the atmosphere 122
The dangers of comparative biochemistry 124
Chapter X. THE ORIGIN OF LIFE AND ITS LATER EVOLUTION . . 126
Evolution and paleontology 126
Seven assumptions 127
Possibility of multiple biogenesis 129
Chapter XI. CONCLUSIONS 131
What we know 131
What we shall never know 134
What further research may teach us 135
Closing remark 135
REFERENCES 137
INDEX 141

CHAPTER I

INTRODUCTION

INTEREST IN THE ORIGIN OF LIFE ON EARTH

In my position as a naturalist specialised in geology, the origin of life on earth, and particularly its geological aspects, ought to have interested me from early days. This has not been the case. Quite to the contrary, my early interests were captured by other fascinating aspects of the geological history of the earth, to such an extent that the origin of life remained outside my personal vision. Not until much later, and then only through a lucky coincidence, did I become aware of this subject. This lucky event came about by a certain number of searching questions asked by the late microbiologist, Professor A. Kluyver of Delft.

Only then did I realise how much thought was given in modern biology, mainly by microbiologists and biochemists, to the mode of origin of life on earth. Concurrently I realised that geology has to consider its own attitude towards this new development. Not only must we study our own findings and how they can be incorporated into the viewpoints of the biologists, but we must also think about the direction to which geological research might be oriented to help unravel this subject.

I believe my case to be typical for most geologists. Consequently, this book is to inform them about the problems concerning the origin of life, problems which for the greater number of geologists are outside the daily routine. On the other hand, many biologists want to know what geologists are thinking about these problems, and what factual data geology has to offer. It is mainly for these two groups that this book has been written. However, I hope to have succeeded in giving enough of the basic trends of research and of speculative thinking to make it of interest also to the more general reader.

The origin of life on earth has a far wider appeal than to special-

ised geologists and biologists only. It is, so to speak, at the base of
the everyday life of you and me and everybody.

There is, of course, also a special interest to religious people. To
many churchmen of all denominations the dilemma of creation or
development of life on earth through natural causes is a prime
question, which might touch at the very heart of religion. As a
geologist I have tried to set forth clearly the facts we know and the
methods we use, in our mode of thinking, to combine these facts into
mental pictures. As a geologist I have, of course, not touched upon
possible repercussions of these pictures on religious teaching. But I
think I have attained my goal when my side of this problem — the
findings of a naturalist with a special training in geology — is com-
municated comprehensibly to the interested reader.

GEOLOGISTS AND THE ORIGIN OF LIFE

Before proceeding any further, I think it would be best to look into
the backgrounds, and reach an understanding of the negative attitude
many geologists have towards the problems concerning the origin of
life on earth.

Geologic history covers an enormous time-span and the problems
it poses to the geologist are as interesting and varied as they are
often difficult to solve. An answer to each and every question can
generally only be attempted after much painstaking work: work of
a highly romantic character, it is true; work in the field, in actual
mapping and investigating rugged mountains or impenetrable jungles;
work, it follows, which greatly taxes the scientists energy and which
must, moreover, be followed up in the laboratory by equally time-
consuming microscopic and chemical studies of rock samples and by
the identification and classification of the fossils collected.

Consequently geologists tend to concentrate on those problems that
seem relatively easy to solve, and for which enough material facts
are at hand. Among the problems relating to the history of life on
earth, over the geological past, this has led to a concentrated effort
on the study of the later evolution of life. Although the paleontological record is horrifyingly incomplete, still, life on earth has
supplied us with its fossilised representatives for the last half billion
years. This offers ample working material for any number of paleont-
ologists for years to come.

In comparison, geological data about the origin of life, which reaches even farther back in time, are scanty in the extreme. The whys and wherefores will be set forth in this book, but the fact remains that there are incomparably more data about the later evolution of life on earth than about its earliest period.

Moreover, in this particular case the resistance must be recalled which research into the history of life on earth in the geological past has encountered from churchpeople. Views on the history of life on earth, be it the origin through natural causes or "only" its further natural evolution, have been, and are still in some cases, an anathema to many of the stricter church members, clergy and laity alike. Geologists, in trying to overcome this dogmatic barrier against their legitimate scientific research, of course concentrated on their strongest case; that is, on the evolution of life during the last half billion years.

In this same vein, it so happened that geologists became aware of the fact that often natural evolution is more easily reconciled with popular versions of church dogma when in conjunction with some nebulous beginning, some *generatio spontanea,* then when coupled with views on natural processes governing all life, including its origin. Creation, in the views first indicated, is separate from natural evolution. During discussions following lectures on the evolution of life on earth, I often got the impression that in this way creation can be accepted on the faith of the church; natural evolution on the faith of the paleontological record. Even here, the difficulties have been great. Moreover, they showed a marked variation with the kind of evolution studied. Just as in many schools sexual problems may be taught as long as one only deals with poppies and bees, and perhaps even with the horse, whilst this subject is taboo with monkeys and man, evolutionary viewpoints encountered more resistance the nearer to man the examples were chosen. I know of a world-famous paleontologist, who in public addresses still does not want any discussion after his talk when he speaks on the origin of man, but is quite willing to do so when he has spoken about horses or ammonites.

So on the one hand we geologists have the possibility of studying the evolution of life on earth, of paleontological research, with a wealth of factual data. Although the gaps in the paleontological records are still so large that anyone with a bias can still make a case against natural evolution, the development of paleontological research clearly points towards its general acceptance. Many gaps in the records have been lately filled by lucky finds and we feel sure what this research is leading up to.

On the other hand, there is the problem of the origin of life on earth. Here the data are extremely poor. The time elapsed is so enormous that it is difficult to prove anything at all, because the record is not only incomplete in the extreme, but also often changed beyond recognition by younger events. Moreover, such research implies a doubt towards popular views on creation and thereby provokes criticism on immaterial grounds from the side of churchpeople: criticism which cannot be effectively answered owing to the lack of data.

A certain defeatism consequently reigned in geology. Although perhaps never clearly expressed, the attitude has for a long time been: "Let us study the evolution of life on earth over the last half billion years". This gives us quite enough to do. We may leave the origin of life on earth either to creation or to some *generatio spontanea*. The subject is not ripe for scientific research for want of data. As long as this is the case we scientists had better leave it alone, because it might prove too hot to handle. Everybody can philosophize over it at his own discretion, but we have no real scientific basis from which to start research.

THE BIOLOGICAL APPROACH

This situation has now completely changed. Although in geology, too, we have acquired some very interesting new data, and although the techniques for absolute dating, which will be treated *in extenso* further on, give us a far better geologic understanding of the problem, this has not been the main reason for the complete change in outlook. The real impetus has come from the vast interest biologists have since taken in the subject. An interest which has perceptibly quickened since World War II. It is not geology alone which is now asked for definite answers to this problem. Quite to the contrary, it is biology, mainly basing itself on microbiology and biochemistry, which has arrived at certain definite conceptions and is eagerly pursuing further research. Biology now derives from theoretical grounds a possible mode of origin of life on earth through natural causes. This does not prove that life did really originate on earth in this way. But it provides us with an acceptable hypothesis for further study. The question is now about the geologic setting of the origin of life, about the possibility of the processes postulated by biological research having their place in the geologic history of the earth.

RELIGION AND THE ORIGIN OF LIFE

This question is, of course, still very controversial. It touches the roots of religious and ethical conceptions of every educated person. Undoubtedly, the reason why Russia was a pioneer in the new wave of interest in the origin of life on earth was not purely scientific. Just as there has been resistance from religious circles against research into the history of life, this same research was expressly furthered by Marxist doctrine. Instead of a protection of popular church teachings, the Russian attitude was, of course, prompted by the wish to be able to attack such thinking. The goal was a completely materialistic theory of life, not only of its evolution, but also of its origin. Or, to put it perhaps a little too succinctly, to do away altogether with creation.

I have thought it necessary to discuss this religious, antireligious and ethical background of the problem of the origin of life on earth, just because it so overwhelmingly exists in many minds, and also because it is so difficult to abstract oneself from this background in order to attain as high a measure of objectivity as possible. It has been a pleasant experience for me, when reading the more recent literature on the subject, to note the objective and academic quality of all recent research. The literature seems entirely unbiassed by either Marxist or religious dialectics. It reports on scientific experiments and on theories, several of which still highly speculative, founded along scientific lines of thought on these experiments, or on geological or astronomical phenomena and the hypotheses derived therefrom, in an extremely vigorous way, but based on science alone.

ABOUT THIS BOOK

The object of this book will be, therefore, to put forward in a similarly objective way the facts and theories geology has to offer on this question of the origin of life. Since it appeals not only to geologists, care will be taken to stress the basic assumptions which underlie any presentation of the facts of the earth's history. The origin of life on earth reaches far back into this history. In fact, it goes back even farther than most geologists are personally familiar with. Many popular books on geology have appeared in recent years, and we may assume that many now have some knowledge of geology. Most of these popular books, however, stress only the last half billion years of the earth's history, as do most textbooks. This is the "normal" geology, easy to popularize by a great number of pictures of fossils. Our subject, the origin of life, however, takes us back at least three billion * years. Great care will consequently be taken to stress the differences between this earlier and longer, but far less known period, and the better known and much more popularized later history of "only" the last half billion years.

ACKNOWLEDGMENTS

Many people have helped in the preparation of this book, although only a limited number can be mentioned here. Permission to reproduce figures was granted by Pergamon Press (Figs. 8, 9, 10 and 14), by Professor A. Holmes (Fig. 6) and by Professors M. Gravelle and M. Lelubre and the Société géologique de France (Figs. 25 and 26). Dr. A. Wilson and Professors P. Ramdohr and E. S. Barghoorn also granted their permission, and supplied clean prints for new blocks to be made. Professor Barghoorn sent new unpublished figures of the earliest known fossils, taken by Professor S. A. Tyler and himself.

The typescript was read in part by Professors R. Hooykaas, J. Th. G. Overbeek and H. P. Berlage and by Dr. E. ten Haaf, whilst Mr. P. van der Kruk critically reviewed all of it. Their efforts resulted in definite improvements.

* I have followed the American custom of calling 10^9, or 1,000,000,000, one billion. This is done because absolute dating in geology has been, since World War II, mainly an American science. So in calling a thousand million a billion, I follow the custom of most of the newer literature.

One million years is written as 1 my (1 ma in European literature), 1 billion years is sometimes written as 1 G years (Pirie).

CHAPTER II

UNIFORMITARIANISM AND ACTUALISM

PHILOSOPHIZING ABOUT UNIFORMITARIANISM AND ACTUALISM

The two words heading this chapter have almost the same meaning. They express the assumption of a certain continuity of physical processes in geological history. Anglo-Saxons mainly use the word uniformitarianism, but continental Europeans, in their own languages, denote the same principle with words like *actualisme* (French) or *Aktualismus* (German). These words lend themselves very easily to a sort of pseudo-translation into 'actualism' as the English version.

This notwithstanding, it also happens that the two words highlight two sides of one and the same line of reasoning which is basic to all modern geology. Physical processes, both on the earth and in the earth, are thought to be subject to unchanging natural laws and therefore more or less continuous and uniform over the past; hence the word uniformitarianism. Once this assumption is accepted, one may study actual processes and extrapolate these into the geological past to interpret our factual findings in forming a genetical, historical picture. Hence the word actualism.

Uniformitarianism, or actualism, is opposed to the earlier doctrine of catastrophes, as applied to geologic history.

Before entering further into this matter of continuity *versus* catastrophes, it is best, I think, to introduce a digression about the value of such basic philosophical principles in geology, in order to realise what place such basic lines of thought as uniformitarianism have in geology.

To speak at all about philosophy in context with geology will perhaps seem unfortunate to some, to use an understatement, because only rarely are geologists good philosophers. This in turn stems, I believe, from the fact that the phenomena our great planet offers for study are so immensely varied that no mere description is ever sufficient to convey a complete idea of any of its phases. No mere word picture conveys all the information on even a single exposure of rocks to the man who has not himself seen that spot. This is borne out clearly in every travelogue of a geologist who, visiting for the first time regions about which he may have heard or read extensively, finds that his mental picture was still very nebulous. Take a European geologist to the Appalachians or the Rocky Mountains, or an American to the Alps, the result will be the same. You will hear your man enthuse about his luck to be able to see these areas at last for himself, and so to check by personal inspection his own incomplete and unbalanced impressions from the literature.

In geological descriptions one normally finds only part of the story. Either some main point is stressed, which results in oversimplification, or, more often, exceptional details are diligently pointed out, whilst the author forgets that only a minor part of his audience can really take the general description for granted.

If then it is wellnigh impossible to express oneself in words only, this does not, of course, lead naturally to an aptitude for strong philosophical essays in which ultimate meanings are conveyed by words and by words only. Geologists have the tendency to supply as many illustrations as feasible: photos, maps and sections. The rest one has just to imagine for oneself — a trend crystallized, for instance, in the slogan of a Swiss geologist: "Hingehen und gucken", or "Go there and look".

This digression was included because I think it is necessary to clarify this side of the geological aspect before we proceed with a discussion of uniformitarianism and its bearing on the origin of life on earth. Both uniformitarianism and the earlier doctrine of catastrophism belong to basic geological philosophy. They have been defined and re-defined, they have had their adherents and opposers, but the literature in which either of these basic lines of thought has been expressly treated is scarce. The only, and very thorough, study of uniformitarianism as such is to be found in Professor Hooykaas' book, *Natural Law and Divine Miracle* (Hooykaas, 1960), which was not written by a geologist.

It is, as we shall see, very difficult to give a precise definition of uniformitarianism or actualism. One has to content oneself with a very general outline which leaves room for borderline cases. To most geologists this is not so bad as it might seem, because in practice borderline cases are very limited in number and of no great importance. Practical application of the outline, even in its general form, in most cases presents no difficulties. Difficulties arise, on the other hand, if we try to narrow down our definitions. One might then even arrive at a distinction without there being any difference. We agree with Hooykaas, who in his text stresses the different aspects of 'uniformitarianism' and 'actualism', but in his glossary states that the two words now are synonymous.

I will use the two words as synonyms for this principle of a certain continuity that nowadays underlies all geological philosophy, even if not expressly stated.

CATASTROPHISM AND UNIFORMITARIANISM

As said before, notwithstanding the fact that they have not often been well expressed, the doctrines of catastrophism and of uniformitarianism are basic to geologic thought. Therefore, if we want to evaluate the geologic picture of the early days of the earth in which life originated, we must take note of their meaning in the study of geology. Of the two, the doctrine of catastrophes is the earlier. It has become replaced by uniformitarian lines of thinking largely through the influence of two British geologists, Hutton (1726-1797) and Lyell (1797-1875).

According to the catastrophists, the successive states of the surface of the earth discovered by geology for events from the past, are so vastly different *inter se* and from the present, that only very large catastrophes, suddenly occurring at some points in history, can be the explanation. World-wide sudden inundations and volcanic upheavals were the main catastrophic events. We recognise, of course, the biblical version of the deluge together with the volcanic catastrophe of Vesuvius, as described by Pliny the Younger; 18th and 19th century required reading for any European intellectual.

So what is more sensible than to assume similar catastrophes to interpret geologic phenomena in the past? The erection of a mountain chain then is nothing but a sudden catastrophic upheaval of the earth. Sudden inundations of large parts of the continents were due to floods comparable to the Deluge, and the extinction of a fossil fauna was the result of some other, as yet unknown, fatal catastrophe.

Uniformitarianism does not deny that sudden catastrophes may occur. But they are never world wide, nor is their effect comparable to the gradual changing of the earth due to actualistic processes of small immediate effect, but operating over large time-spans. So into the philosophy of uniformitarianism there entered a conception of the extremely long time-spans available for geologic processes.

TIME IN GEOLOGY

Realisation of the large quantities of time consumed by the geologic history of the earth, gradually helped to form a general acceptance of actualistic thought. In the early days, long before absolute dating techniques were discovered, this was, of course, nothing that could be definitely proved. As so many things in geology, it could only be made to look probable, or perhaps even acceptable, by a rather subjective interpretation of some factual data. More than anything else, I think it is Lyell's description of old temples around Naples, which have been temporarily inundated through slow changes in altitude relative to the water level of the Mediterranean, which sold the idea of the big effect of small causes, if only consistently at work over long enough periods.

Eternity, a Chinese parable tells, can be hinted at in the following way. In a far northern country a rocky mountain is visited once a century by a small bird which, in cleaning, scrapes its bill on the stony hill. When the mountain has been worn down from the scraping of that small bird's bill, once every century, one second of eternity has elapsed. The Chinese poet was no geologist, because a geologist sees a great number of smaller processes continuously operating at present, which, although unnoticed by the casual poet, have a far greater effect than the polishing of that little bird's bill. Amongst others, and when no other forces are at work, mere erosion will wear down that mountain far more quickly.

Time, it follows from this juxtaposition of a Chinese poet and a sceptical geologist, time is the uniformitarianists' biggest ally. Given enough time, earth movements of 1 mm a year, or even 1 mm a century, can create mountains or oceans. Given enough time, a new fauna may develop gradually out of an older one, whilst the older forms die out almost imperceptibly. Given enough time, series of repeated small earthquakes will also build mountains or sink parts of continents to oceanic depths. Or to take another example, a volcano, even if none of its eruptions is as violent as the Plinian eruption of Vesuvius, will in due time bury all of its surroundings completely under lava and volcanic ashes.

When we think of uniformity in regard to the processes governing the development of the earth, we are led astray very easily by the very slow tempo of these processes. In our short-lived human egocentric mind, we think of the earth as stable and strong. Nothing is less true. Whole continents float in a heavier substratum, or, as we say in our scientific jargon, are in isostatic equilibrium. In fact, they seldom attain this equilibrium; in the geologist's eye they are continuously bobbing up and down. Volcanoes continually bring parts of that substratum up to the surface, their work being comparable to a sort of global-scale mole. Meanwhile, all higher hills and mountains are continuously attacked by erosion, whilst the detritus which is chafed off the mountains is laid down in lowland flats and seas.

If we want to compare our own human history with that of the earth, we must completely discard this egocentric thinking, and accept the vast amounts of time of the history of the earth as a common, everyday matter. In comparing the two, we must always keep in mind that one single year in human history corresponds more or less to a million years in the history of the earth.

TIME THROUGH A GEOLOGIST'S EYE

A geologist consequently sees no stable earth, but a constantly moving picture. He sees a jumble of mountains forming, say, the Alps or the Appalachians, only to be immediately attacked by erosion. He may see wide seas expanding over large parts of the continents, whilst elsewhere shallow seas dry up completely and make place for rich continental fauna and flora, perhaps accompanied by spectacular volcanic events. Or, for instance, many geologists even see the continents wandering over the earth's surface, or breaking up and partly foundering to oceanic depths.

This, however, is the view through the geologist's eye, who by a long training has acquired a certain flair for speeding up his mental pictures. One million times acceleration, of course, gives a catastrophic angle to even the slowest motion of processes. So what we must keep in mind, always, is that these spectacular revolutions, these catastrophic events of our old, our very old earth, come about at a snail's pace. Most geologic changes occur at a pace which can be estimated at something between 1 mm per century and 1 mm per year. In this view, most apparent catastrophes in the history of the earth can be explained by normal processes, actually at work on earth. By slow crustal movements, by slow climatic changes, by erosion and sedimentation, by a repetition of volcanic events or earthquakes.

VARIATIONS IN INTENSITY OF PROCESSES: THE PULSE OF THE EARTH

It is not necessary that these actual processes have always been uniform in intensity although they were uniform in kind. To take an example, we know of several Ice Ages in the recent and in the more early geological past. Although an ice-cap extending over most of northwestern Europe and North America is quite a different proposition from the small vestiges of ice-caps now still remaining on Greenland, Iceland and Spitzbergen, the processes of ice-cap formation are not different. There is a difference in extension, or size, only. The local climatic conditions, the surplus of snow fall, the flowing-out of the ice towards the rim of the ice-cap, the formation of moraines, everything one can think of, are the same in both cases. With the actual processes at work in Greenland now, we can interpret the much larger ice-caps which covered northwestern Europe and North America in the recent past. The processes are similar, although of varying intensity.

Conversely, when we find fossils of tropical plants or ancient Dinosaur tracks on Greenland and Spitzbergen, in sediments older than the Ice Age, we conclude that a tropical climate then existed that far north. Not from a sudden catastrophic change of, say, the amount of radiation received from the sun, but through slow changes for which very minor variations in intensity of one or a number of processes now, as before, in operation can be made responsible.

To a geologist, consequently, everything is in motion. We speak of "our unstable Earth" or of "our moving Earth". But not only this; we also recognize definite periods of a slower or a quicker tempo of certain processes. This has been most concisely expressed in the title of Professor Umbgrove's textbook *The Pulse of the Earth*. But even such a pulse-beat is, as we saw, not due to catastrophes but only to small changes in the intensity of slow actual processes.

SCHEMATIZATION IN GEOLOGIC WRITING

To those who still want to see something catastrophic in a regular beating of a pulse of the earth, I might be allowed to point out once more that the period of this terrestrial pulse excludes all comparison with catastrophes in a human sense. One pulse-beat of the earth, in the sense as described by Umbgrove, takes about 250 million years. So what is a day or a year or even man's life span in comparison to one beat of the pulse of our earth?

Not every geologist adheres to Professor Umbgrove's picture of a strict synchronization of many different processes in the earth to a pulse beat of 250 million years. Of course, extrapolation from the present is so large that many differences of opinion may arise. However, apart from doubts about the strictness of synchronization and the exact length of the individual periods in earlier parts of the earth's history, time spans of 250 million years, more or less, are quite well established for many different sorts of variations in intensity of geological phenomena. Umbgrove's theory of many different terrestrial processes, regularly varying together with such extreme slowness will, on the other hand, most forcibly instil into a non-geologist this distinction between human history and that of the earth.

Of course, one cannot all the time stress the importance of these immense time-spans in geological writing, and it is here that many geologists perhaps too freely express what their imagination sees when looking at the slow history of the earth through eyes expressly trained to speed up this development one million times. Every amateur who has taken slow-motion pictures will know what a factor of one million in speed-up implies.

To illustrate this, I will take just one example from geologic literature: the process of mountain building or orogeny. The creation of our present major mountain chains, such as the Alps, the Himalayas and the Andes, has taken some 50 million years. Earth movements over that period were of the 1 mm a year type. Before that time the earth's crust was much more quiet, and movements of the order of 1 mm per century were normal. Moreover, this earlier, more stable period was of much longer duration. It lasted something between 100 million or 200 million years.

We geologists now are apt to speak, in our speeded-up version of the history of the earth, of a 'catastrophic period of mountain building', or of 'revolutions of the earth's crust', when describing that relatively short, relatively unstable period of mountain building which 'only' lasted some 50 million years. We like to stress the difference between this later period of mountain building and the earlier, longer, more stable period. In doing so, perhaps for lack of words, perhaps also owing to a sort of laziness, we definitely tend to overstress. We often forget to state explicitly that our catastrophes, the catastrophic events in geological literature, are a far cry from human catastrophes. Our catastrophic mountain building period, to return to the example mentioned, was the ultimate result only of many repeated small-scale movements summed up over 50 million years.

No geologist will therefore deny the mobility of the earth, or the existence of variations in speed or in intensity of the different processes in operation on earth. Nevertheless, it forms no objection for him to adhere to an actualistic viewpoint on geologic history, or to use present causes in explaining the past.

SMALLER CATASTROPHES AND UNIFORMITARIANISM

To make matters still more difficult to express, in relation to this principle of uniformitarianism, it must be added that even smaller catastrophes, although real enough on our human scale, take their place in this actualistic picture of the geologic past. To take the two examples mentioned above, the biblical deluge and the Plinian eruption of Vesuvius, we feel sure that many similar catastrophes have contributed to the history of the earth.

Floods, for instance, are quite common smaller catastrophes. They may be the results of quite different physical causes. We have rain floods and river floods, such as in Mesopotamia; tsunamis due to seaquakes, as in the Pacific; storm floods as in the low-lying coastal districts of Holland. These and other causes all produce floods of local catastrophic consequences. Each larger flood, regardless of its cause, may have entered into the saga of a certain tribe, and eventually might have become extrapolated to effects far beyond that of the original, or schematized into Gospel truth. None of them will, however, at one single time, have altered the earth's surface to any extent. Only when such floods occur repeatedly will they very gradually, acquire geological significance.

The same can be said for volcanic eruptions. Even the Plinian

eruption of Vesuvius destroyed no more than three cities, Herculaneum, Pompei and Stabiae, all situated on its southwestern flank.
No more than a quarter of the surface of a single volcano was
affected by this eruption. The rest of Roman Empire lived on, I will
not say happily, but still without any interruption. Had not Pliny
the Younger lost his uncle in the event, it is very much to be doubted
if we would have such a detailed account, even of this major eruption.

So, a flood here, a quake there, with a volcanic eruption thrown
in, this is all compatible with uniformitarianism. Such smaller catastrophes result from actual processes at work on earth. They do not
reach a global scale.

I believe that to drive home this local character of human catastrophes, both in areal extent and in time, we can best return to the
text of Lyell's *Principles*. In the closing remarks of his first volume,
following a description of the ravages from volcanic activity in the
Naples district, we read: 'The signs of changes imprinted on it during
this period may appear in after-ages to indicate a series of un-
parallelled disasters ... If they who study these phenomena ... consider the numerous proofs of reiterated catastrophes to which the
region was subject, they might, perhaps, commiserate the unhappy
state of beings condemned to inhabit a planet during its nascent and
chaotic state, and feel grateful that their favoured race has escaped
such scenes of anarchy and misrule'.

However, pursuing Lyell's narrative, we read: 'What was the real
condition of Campania [Napolitana] during those years of dire conclusion? "A climate", says Forsyth, "where Heaven's breath smells
sweet and wooingly — a vigorous and luxuriant nature unparalleled
in its productions — a coast which was once the fairy-land of poets,
and the favourite retreat of great men. Even the tyrants of the creation loved this alluring region, spared it, adorned it, lived in it, died
in it." The inhabitants, indeed, have enjoyed no immunity from the
calamities which are the lot of mankind; but the principal evils
which they have suffered must be attributed to moral, not to physical,
causes — to disastrous events over which man might have exercised
a control, rather than to the inevitable catastrophes which result
from subterranean agency. When Spartacus encamped his army of
ten thousand gladiators in the old extinct crater of Vesuvius, the

Fig. 1. View of the Bay of Balae, near Naples, where volcanic eruptions and slow crustal movements induced Lyell to the classical remarks on uniformitarianism (from the original drawing by Lyell, 1875).

Fig. 2. The so-called Temple of Serapis at Pozzuoli, near Naples, which plays a prominent part in the narrative of Lyell owing to its prehistoric and historic changes in altitude (from the original drawing by Lyell, 1875).

volcano was more justly a subject of terror to Campania than it has ever been since the rekindling of its fires (Lyell, 1875, Vol. I, pp. 654-655).

This emphasizes the difficulty of giving a strict definition of uniformitarianism. To take the floods: a flood of 1 m high is quite a normal thing. A flood 10 m high is already rather exeptional, when measured against the short experience of our own life span. But we would be at a loss to say if a flood 100 m high was still due to actual causes, if we ever found evidence for such a catastrophic deluge in geological history. Luckily for the geologist this difficulty, as I already indicated above, does not occur in the practical application of actualism. Floods are normally between 1 m and 10 m high, volcanoes normally destroy only part of their surroundings during one single eruption, and even the worst of quakes are very limited in the areal extent of their damage. Only by continuous repetition, not over short time-spans such as centuries, but over thousands and millions of years, do such major catastrophes in a human sense, but quite minor catastrophes in a geological sense, acquire global significance.

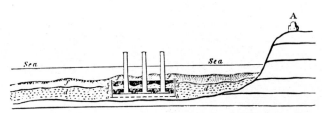

Fig. 3. Section through the so-called Temple of Serapis at Pozzuoli, near Naples, showing the various layers with which it has been covered, together with its deepest inundation as witnessed by the boreholes of marine organisms on its pillars (from Lyell, 1875). *a b*. Ancient mosaic pavement. *c c*. Dark marine incrustation. *d d*. First filling up shower of ashes. *e e*. Freshwater calcareous deposit. *f f*. Second filling up. A. Stadium.

UNIFORMITARIANISM AND ITS IMPLICATIONS FOR THE ORIGIN OF LIFE

Hence, for all practical purposes, and leaving out philosophical considerations, we may define actualism or uniformitarianism as the tendency in geology to interpret facts of the history of the earth by the same processes as we know or assume to be at work now on or in the earth. It must, however, be explicitly stated that the intensity of such processes may have varied over the time-span of geologic history.

The implications of uniformitarianism for our search into the origin of life on earth are clear. We look for natural causes of the same character as are in operation at present. We do not envisage some sudden event, by which life appeared all at once as a fully fledged phenomenon on every corner of the earth. The origin of life will have covered an enormous time-span, if measured against human standards. During this period development will have been slow, almost beyond imagination.

In its slowness, however, the origin of life may well have been infinitely varied. For all we know, there may have been different parallel series of development. Possibly only a small number of these, or perhaps even only one single line of development, led to our present life.

In its slowness, moreover, the origin of life will have been subject to the same physical and chemical laws as life is today. As we shall see later, it is probable that our atmosphere, rivers and oceans are quite different now from what they were in those years long past — in those early years when the real "struggle for life", that for its origin, took place. But even if the environment was quite different, so different as to be unrecognizable by present-day standards, the laws of nature were the same. This permits us to extrapolate the findings of present-day microbiology and biochemistry into that distant past, as indicative of the environment in which the origin of life took place.

In exploring the geological aspects of the origin of life, we have now made an important stride. We have arrived at an understanding of how geology works, how it arrives at its conclusions about events long past. We found that the basic principle of uniformitarianism underlies geologic studies, and what its implications are. In doing so we became impressed by the enormous amount of time elapsed since the early days of geologic history. It is now time to gain some idea of how these time-spans are measured in gelogy, and what is the reliability of such measurements. The next chapter consequently will deal with this side of the geological aspects of the origin of life.

Chapter III

MEASURING TIME IN GEOLOGY

RELATIVE AND ABSOLUTE DATING

Measuring time in geology is a young science — even for geology, which is itself one of the youngest of natural sciences. Two decades ago the first comprehensive volume on this subject appeared, the highly original *Dating the Past* of Professor Zeuner of London. The same title could well have served as a heading for this chapter. It is, however, not fear of plagiarism which led me to choose another heading. Instead, the difference in wording is meant to convey the extremely rapid development over the last twenty years of the science of measuring the time elapsed during the geological periods.

Professor Zeuner gave full attention to various methods of measuring time, as they then existed. But apart from the actual counting of years, as applied in dendrochronology, where the yearly growth rings of trees are examined, or in the so-called varved clays, which also exhibit a clear yearly sequence of coarser and finer layers, the methods now employed were still in their infancy. These newer methods are all based on radioactive decay of various natural elements. Two decades ago, they were still in the process of development. It was only by the postwar advance in electronic instrumentation that they gained a practical value for geology.

Still, it is well to stress that even so short a time ago Zeuner's book was a considerable step forward in that it focussed attention on the possibilities existing for real dating, for measuring in years the time elapsed since certain geological phenomena took place. Until then, practically all 'dating' in geology was still done by the time-honoured method in which only a relative age was established.

This is, of course, common knowledge for a geologist. But just because it is such common, everyday usage, this relativity of most geologic dating is not always properly stated. As we are interested in this book not in facts alone but also in how they have been arrived at, I think it is well to thrash out properly the distinction between the normal everyday geological method of relative dating, and the means we now possess to measure geological time in absolute terms, in years, or millions, or billions of years.

RELATIVE DATING

Again we must stress the fact that in dating the past, normal everyday geology only supplies a relative or comparative age. The methods used today essentially go back to the time of the English surveyor and engineer William Smith (1769-1831). They are based on two main tenets, *viz.* the *Principle of Superposition* on the one hand, and *Fauna Evolution in Geologic Time* on the other.

Principle of superposition

The principle of superposition quite simply states that in any pile of sedimentary rock, one bed was laid down after the other, each bed being sedimented on top of the next underlying bed. The younger bed is thus always superposed on the older, hence the name of this principle. In this way a relative age can be assigned to a succession of layers of rock, found, for instance, in a hill scarp or in a bore hole. If it is possible to recognize the same succession in other hill sides or bore holes, a correlation is established. And if in the latter localities other beds are exposed, either older beds underneath the known series, or younger beds on their top, then the local relative time-table can even be extended.

In some areas — for instance, in the London and Paris basins, which among others formed a starting point for this type of age determination — it is possible to follow such successions over quite long distances along the hill sides. But any interruption of such a series of exposures, for instance, a broad alluvial valley, a lake or an ocean, limits the application of this method. It is often difficult or impossible to tell which layer on one side of the gap is exactly to be correlated with a given layer on the other side. This holds true, for example, even for a narrow gap like the English Channel. The white chalk cliffs of Dover and of Cap Blanc Nez, which look exactly similar at first sight, already show many details in their lithological succession which cannot be correlated across the intervening water body.

Organic evolution

It is here that organic, faunal and floral, evolution comes in. Sediments laid down at the same time in the geological history may contain fossilized remnants of the contemporary fauna and flora. Because most groups of higher organisms show evolution over the geological past, there were at any time definite forms which lived only at that time. If these are sufficiently distinct from both their ancestors and their descendants, so as to enable us to recognize them specifically from their fossilized parts, organic evolution kindly supplied geologists with what are called index fossils. By comparing such fossils, comparative ages for widely separated rock sections can be established. The fact that most often 'fauna evolution' is used in this context, when indeed 'organic evolution' both of the fauna and of the flora is meant, stems from the circumstance that a far greater number of such index fossils come from extinct faunae than from extinct florae. This is mainly dictated by the very nature of the fossilization process, which favours strongly the preservation of recognizable parts of animals over plants.

The basic idea of using organic evolution to date the geologic past, be it in a relative way, is thus delightfully simple. Why then, anyone familiar with geologists or geology will ask, is there divergence of opinion among geologists about almost any long-distance age comparison? The reason is that, although the basic idea is simple, its implementation is crowded with difficulties. Not only have similar lines of development been repeated in many groups of organisms throughout geologic time, so that some groups of organisms may show remarkable resemblances to forms which were not directly related and that lived much earlier or later, but also, most fossils do not occur in all sediments formed in one given time interval, because living things tend to concentrate in areas which are suitable for them. Moreover, many groups with a relatively rapid organic evolution, which, of course, supply the best material for later index fossils, do not occur in large numbers of individuals, and consequently their fossilized remains are rare.

Eras of relative age in geology

However, such details do not affect us in our understanding of how geology dates the past. We may safely leave the details of the implementation of the principle of organic evolution to the efforts of the stratigrapher and the paleontologist, whose concern they are. Suffice it to say that by painstaking use of these two guiding principles, those of superposition and of organic evolution, an impressive body of facts has been assembled. These facts permit dating the geologic past in the relative time scale. All the commonly used divisions of geologic time and also the main eras of Paleozoic, Mesozoic and Cenozoic or Neozoic are based on evolutionary changes of life, or, to be more exact, on the evolution of the fauna. Even the names just mentioned, which divide geologic past into the eras of the Early, Middle and the New Animal World — a division comparable to Early History, Middle Ages and Newer History — even these names indicate that these periods and their limits were defined by the contemporary fauna, whilst the ancient flora plays only a subordinate part in relative geologic dating.

Moreover, just as in human history, there are also geological prehistoric and protohistoric periods, in which dating by organic evolution is impossible, in the same way as normal historic methods are of no avail in human prehistory and protohistory.

As we shall see, our quest as to the origin of life on earth will eventually lead us into this earlier geological history. Before continuing, however, let me stress firmly once more that all normal dating in geology is of a relative nature only. It tells us, for instance, that beds of the Mesozoic are younger than beds of the Paleozoic. It tells us that beds of the younger Cenozoic are very much younger than beds of the early Paleozoic. But never is it possible from this method of dating alone to state something like 'the Mesozoic began umpteen million years ago'. Any statement giving a definite number of years is based on the methods of absolute dating, and not on the normal geologic way of relative dating of the past.

Relative age of sediments and igneous rocks

One more fact has to be put forward in relation to this relative dating of the geologic past: it can only be applied directly to sediments. Igneous rocks, formed within the crust through the gradual cooling and solidifying of molten magma, do not follow the principle of superposition. Molten magma tends to break through the crust and thus defies the superposition law. And even when poured out from a volcano over surrounding sediments as lava, thus following the principle of superposition, magma does not contain living organisms. Without fossils, the second guiding principle, that of organic evolution, cannot be applied. So, in normal geologic dating, the age of igneous rocks is doubly relative: it can only be determined relative to the relative age of adjacent sediments. Igneous rocks are always younger than the sediments through which they penetrate. Conversely, igneous rocks are older than sediments by which they are covered. Geologic dating of igneous rocks consequently is always relative to the age of sediments, whose own age is already relative.

ABSOLUTE DATING

Absolute dating, in contrast to the relative dating methods normally used in geology, measures time in years or in larger units. Two of the methods used in absolute dating actually measure time in years. These are dendrochronology and the study of varved clays or other varved deposits. In dendrochronology the year rings of trees, formed through seasonal growth, are counted. In varved clays seasonal layers of finer and coarser clay, deposited during winter and summer in front of an ice-cap, can also be counted. This method has also been successfully applied to, for example, annual layers found in certain rock-salt deposits. But both dendrochronology and the varved sediments can be applied only to time-spans of some tens of thousands of years at the utmost. They are of no importance at all in dating the origin of life on earth. This took place so long ago that we have to measure time in units of millions and even billions of years.

Physical clocks: radioactive decay series

Measuring time-spans of such magnitude is only possible by employing 'physical clocks', based on the continuous radioactive decay of natural elements. All heavier natural elements are unstable, and so are several isotopes of the lighter elements. They only exist at this day because their decay is so slow that the age of the earth, or the age of the rocks in which they are found, is small compared with their decay time.

A single atom of a radioactive isotope decays by a spontaneous process, whose instant of occurrence is not predictable. Only when large numbers of atoms of a radioactive isotope are present, will statistical laws govern the overall decay process. The probability that a given fraction will decay in a certain time is constant for each radioactive isotope. In that case it is possible to state how the total number of radioactive atoms of a given isotope will decrease with time. As the disintegration of individual atoms is random, the rate of decay is proportional only to the number of parent atoms. This constant of proportionality is called the decay constant. The decay rate of a radioactive isotope is conveniently expressed in terms of its half-life. This is the time for any number of atoms of that isotope to decay to one half its original value (Russel and Farquar, 1960).

Constancy of radioactive decay

In all methods using radioactive decay for the measurement of time in geological periods, there is one basic assumption. This is that the decay rate did not vary even over these very long periods. Now theoretical physics tells us this is so. According to theoretical physics, radioactive decay is a nuclear process, which is innate in a given atomic nucleus. Unlike the configuration of the peripheral electrons, which determine the chemical properties of an atom, the nuclear constitution cannot be changed through external influences. Neither heat, cold, pressure nor changes in the electrical or magnetic field, all of which have changed within certain rather narrow limits during the history of the earth, have any influence on a nuclear process such as radioactive decay. Experimental physics corroborates this doctrine of theoretical physics, within the limits of the experiments devised so far. The limits in geology, however, are not the extremes of heat or cold, of gravity or of earth magnetics, or even of extreme pressures. But one essential factor can never be duplicated in the laboratory, *i.e.* the extreme length of time connate to geological processes.

Is it justified, a geologist will ask, to extrapolate the doctrine of nuclear physics, a science barely twenty years old, to geologic eras some billions of years in duration?

Pleochroitic rings

Geology itself supplies an answer to this question in the curious phenomenon of the pleochroitic rings. Many minerals contain darkly coloured spots, which under the microscope appear as a number of

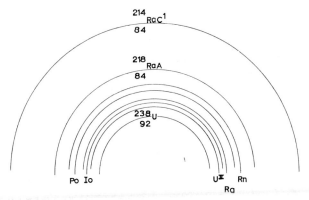

Fig. 4. Schematic drawing of the pleochroitic rings around an inclusion of uranium. In normal rock-forming minerals the radius of the outer sphere of RaC¹ is about 30μ.

concentric rings (Fig. 4). In polarised light these rings show different colour schemes from the host mineral, especially when rotated under the polarising microscope; hence the name pleochroitic rings. These rings are caused by irregularities in the crystal lattice of the host mineral. And these, in turn, are due to various emissions from small inclusions of decaying radioactive elements. Now in a given decay process, the emanation accompanying the decay of a certain radio-active element always has the same energy, because this is a nuclear property innate to the type of atom constituting that element. A certain emanation will always penetrate the same distance in the crystal lattice of the host mineral. It will form a spherical zone of disruption around the radioactive inclusion in the host mineral. In a thin section of the rock, under the microscope, this sphere will, of course, appear as a ring or a perfect circle. Now if ever the energy of the emission of an inclusion of radioactive matter should have changed throughout the life history of a given host mineral, it would not have produced sharply outlined spheres of disturbance within that host mineral. A slow change of energy of the radioactive decay over the millions of years would have resulted in a blurred spot, not in discrete rings. Therefore, because we find so many pleochroitic

28 MEASURING TIME IN GEOLOGY

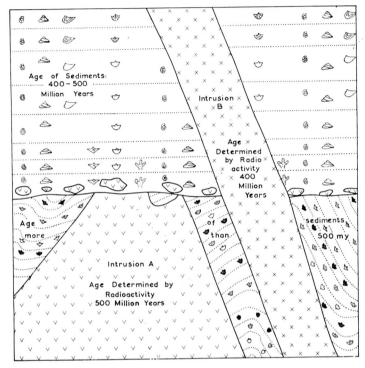

Fig. 5. Scheme of relative and absolute dating in geology. A pile of older sediments has been folded during an orogeny. At the end of the crogenetic period magma intruded into the sediments. This now forms the igneous rocks of intrusion A. The folded crust was later eroded and denudated, whereupon a pile of younger sediments was laid down. This contains pebbles of the igneous rock of intrusion A at its base, so intrusion A is older relative to the younger series of sediments. Both the older and the younger rocks were later intruded by a second magma. A relative age of beds of the younger sediments can be established locally by nothing the superposition of individual beds. Regionally a relative age can be established by the use of index fossils found in this series. The same method can also be applied to older series of sediments. Although the series was folded, it is still possible to see what is the upper and what is the lower bed. It still contains recognizable index

rings with sharp boundaries in many different minerals, we can feel safe that the constants of radioactive decay have, indeed, not changed, even over the extremely long period of geological history.

Consequently, it is almost certain that the physical clocks operating on the decay of natural radioactive elements really give absolute dates. It is, however, somewhat presumptive to say that they date in years. The clocks have been working at the same rate over the billions of years, but our methods of reading them are still far from the reliability achieved in laboratory physics. In rocks we are never quite sure that we do really measure exactly the remaining amount of the parent mineral, nor all the atoms of the ultimate stable element actually produced by the radioactive decay. Consequently an error of, say, 5 per cent may be expected in quite good rock age measurements. This margin, in a rock one billion years old, would still leave us with an uncertainty of fifty million years.

So the normal geologic methods, which ascertain the stratigraphic sequence of relatively older and younger rocks, cannot altogether be replaced by absolute dating techniques. Instead, the latter only supply us with a number of fixes in which our relative stratigraphical data can be arranged. In modern geological dating both methods, absolute and relative, must go hand in hand.

Absolute age of igneous rocks and sediments

Moreover, all absolute dating of older rocks is made on igneous rocks and ore minerals, and not on sediments. With this method, it is possible to establish the birthday of a given igneous rock or ore mineral. This means that we take the age of an igneous rock to be the time elapsed since it crystallized from a molten magma in the earth's crust, and with an ore mineral the time elapsed since it was

---

fossils, which have not been obliterated by metamorphosis accompanying the orogeny.

The relative age of intrusion A is : younger than the lower series of sediments, and older than the upper series. The relative age of intrusion B is : younger than the upper sediments and a great deal younger than the lower sediments.

Absolute dating is possible for the two intrusions. The absolute age of the sediments can, however, only be approximated as either older or younger than the dated intrusions.

deposited from vapours or solutions in the vein in the mine in which it was found. At that date in ideal cases, radioactive elements are incorporated in the minerals of igneous rocks and ore veins, and from that date the decay products of the radioactive elements are, again under ideal circumstances, imprisoned and preserved within the rock or the vein. So, by measuring the amount of parent element left, together with the amount of daughter element produced, and by applying the half-life formula characteristic for this decay process, we arrive at the 'age' of the rock or the ore vein.

Sediments, on the other hand, might contain any amount of decay products from earlier radioactive cycles, washed into the sediment at its formation. They are only suitable for radioactive dating when they contain minerals which formed during the process of sedimentation. Moreover, those 'authigenic' or newly formed minerals must have radioactive elements incorporated. An example, at present the only one used, is the mineral glauconite. This is a complex silicate, containing potassium. Its normal form is greenish grains which form on the bottom of warm, shallow seas, presumably under some biochemical control which is as yet not well-known. Glauconite dating is, however, possible for younger sediments only, less than half a billion years of age. It does not apply to the earlier periods of the earth's history in which the origin of life on earth is situated.

For these older periods, we consequently may state that all absolute dating is done on igneous rocks and ore veins, to the exclusion of sediments.

Radioactive decay series in geology

There are now four radioactive decay processes in use for the dating of older rocks. They have been summarized in Table I. In order of ascending atom number of the parent element, they are the potassium-argon method, the rubidium-strontium method, and the thorium-lead and uranium-lead methods. The latter, although starting from three different radioactive parent elements, thorium and two different uranium isotopes, and although their decay processes are quite different, are always used together, because they have the same stable daughter element, lead. There is a difference, however, in that all three produce a different isotope of lead, as shown in Table I. On this fact the modern refinement of this method of absolute dating is based.

TABLE I

DECAY PROCESSES OF NATURAL RADIOACTIVE ELEMENTS USED IN
ABSOLUTE GEOLOGIC DATING

Parent element	Decay process	Half-life	Final stable isotope
$^{40}_{19}K$ potassium *	Electron capture	$12,4.10^9$ y	$^{40}_{18}A$ argon
$^{87}_{37}Rb$ rubidium	Electron or β ray emission	50.10^9 y	$^{87}_{38}Sr$ strontium
$^{232}_{92}Th$ thorium	Many intermediate steps (Compare Fig. 5)	$13,9.10^9$ y	$^{208}_{82}Pb$ lead
$^{235}_{92}U$ uranium		$0,7.10^9$ y	$^{207}_{82}Pb$ lead
$^{238}_{92}U$ uranium		$4,5.10^9$ y	$^{206}_{82}Pb$ lead

* $^{40}_{19}K$ denotes : $\begin{array}{l} 40 = \text{atomic weight} \\ K = \text{atomic symbol} \\ 19 = \text{atomic number} \end{array}$

Of these various methods the uranium-lead and thorium-lead measurements are the oldest. Only after World War II has better instrumentation, *e.g.* more accurate and more dependable mass spectographs and spectrometers, led to techniques suitable for measuring the other decay series. Moreover, the lead methods have also been immensely improved.

Isotopes

Before the war, a sample had to contain uranium, thorium and lead in large quantities for it to be suitable material for an absolute age determination. Such samples, *e.g.* pitchblende, a highly complex and partly amorphous uranium mineral, were analysed for their uranium, thorium and lead contents. From the respective decay rates of the uranium and thorium series, it was calculated what percentage of the lead present ought to be attributed to the decay of uranium

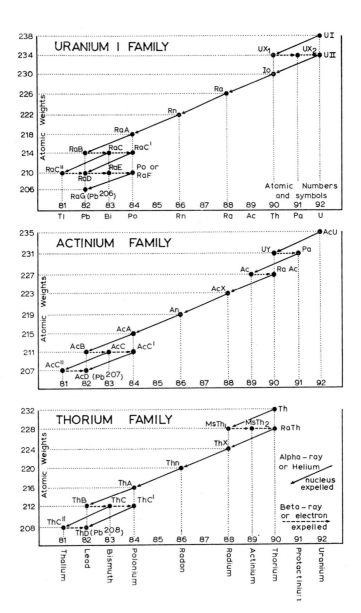

and thorium respectively. Assuming that all lead found was formed only by these two decay processes, the age of a sample could be 'established' by using the formula for the half-life of the two parent minerals.

This obviously made little sense, amongst other reasons, because lead not only contains the radiogenic isotopes ^{206}Pb, ^{207}Pb and ^{208}Pb, which are the end-products of the decay of uranium and thorium, but also the isotope ^{204}Pb, which is not radiogenic at all.

Of course, at that time one was aware of the fallibility of this assumption. But little sense is better than no sense at all. The method was used, simply because there was no better one. Later work has shown that most of the early measurements were far off the mark; but, at that time, they served a definite purpose. They gave the first more or less trustworthy indication of the stupendous length of geologic time. In the early days of absolute dating, this fact was already of paramount importance. Geologists, physicists and astronomers had stressed and re-stressed their conclusions that the age of the earth and of the universe must be inconceivably long. Here were the first direct measurements of the age of rocks, of matter that one could touch, which actually were that old.

Mass spectrometry

Because of the importance absolute dating has for an evaluation of the setting in which the origin of life on earth took place, I had better explain the workings of mass spectrometry a little further. Many readers will be interested to know just what is the basis of these absolute datings, covering such tremendously long periods. The reader who is not interested in this somewhat more technical aspect can skip the following pages and resume the narrative in the final remarks of this chapter. He must, in that case, accept these dates at their face value, even if he is a little dubious about such statements.

As mentioned above, the basic instrument now in use in absolute dating is the mass spectrograph or the mass spectrometer. In it individual atoms are separated according to their mass or atomic weight. Of a given sample the relative amounts of atoms of various

Fig. 6. The decay rates of the uranium, actinium and thorium series of natural radioactive elements (from Holmes, 1937).

mass, the spectrum of the masses of atoms, can be detected. The difference between these two types of instrument is that in a mass spectrograph the atoms of different mass fall on different spots of a photographic plate, whereas in the spectrometer they pass through collimator slits and are counted separately by an electronic device. In the spectrograph the relative amount of the various isotopes is measured by the intensity of the dark spots they produce on the photographic plate. So, basically, the instruments are quite similar, but the mass spectrometer is much more sensitive.

Mass spectrometric methods are described in many textbooks. For our study we will follow the lucid treatment of Russel and Farquar (1960). Mass spectrometers are used mainly to distinguish between isotopes of a single element, or more generally between various kinds of atoms which are very close in their properties. Isotopes of one element, let it once more be stated explicitly, are identical in chemical properties. All atoms of the various isotopes together form that element. Their only difference lies in their atomic weight. They are identical in atomic number and in their peripheral electrons, which determine their chemical properties.

However, because of this very slight difference in atomic weight, isotopes of one element show very slight differences in physical properties, such as temperature and pressure of their boiling point, etc. Most of these differences are, however, too small to form a basis for reliable quantitative determination of relative amounts of isotopes.

The best technique in use today is the deflection of electrically charged particles passing through a magnetic field. Such particles, in this case the electrically charged individual atoms or ions of the isotopes under study, will undergo a force perpendicular to the magnetic field and to their own path, and proportional to their own mass. In a uniform magnetic field ions of the same mass flying perpendicular to that field with the same velocity, will describe a circular path.

In practice, a beam of ions of varying mass is sent through a high-vacuum tube, perpendicular to a constant and uniform magnetic field. Upon entering the tube, the ions are accelerated by an electrical high-potential field V, from which they all acquire the same energy $\frac{1}{2} mv^2$. Their trajectory through the tube will show slight differences in radius, which are related to their mass by the formula

$$m = e \cdot \frac{R^2 \ B^2}{2 \ V}$$

where m = atomic mass, e = ion electric charge, R = radius of ion trajectory in the high-vacuum tube, and B = magnetic field strength. The number of ions of different mass which, after describing slightly divergent trajectories, fall on the collimator slit at the end of the tube, is counted by the electronic set-up.

Mass spectrometers are easiest to work with vapour mixtures. The samples of lead or any other element of which the relative isotopic composition must be ascertained, are introduced as a suitably ionized gaseous chemical compound. They leak through a small orifice into

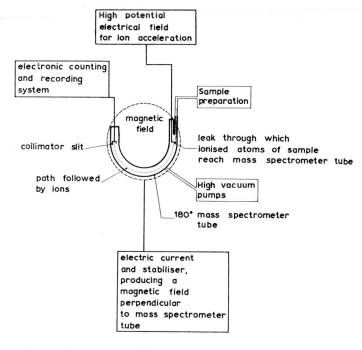

Fig. 7. Diagram of a 180° gas-source mass spectrometer.

the high vacuum of the instrument proper, at which time they are accelerated by the high-potential electric field.

The basic construction of a mass spectrometer is schematized in Fig. 7. A mass spectrometer consists of three units. At the beginning there is the system for handling the samples. This is purely a chemical apparatus, in which the samples are purified, enriched and converted into the gaseous compound suitable for mass spectrometry. Then follows the actual instrument tube, which is often small compared with the accessory parts. At the end of the tube is the ponderous electronic equipment which counts the separate ions that either fall on a number of collimator slots, or are plied over a single slot at the end of the high-vacuum tube by suitable variations of the magnetic field strength. These counts are amplified and recorded in such a way that the mass spectrometer gives an answer that does not require any further processing.

Isotope dilution

In contrast with the cruder pre-war methods, which were prevalently chemical, it follows that mass spectrometry uses the physical differences of the nuclei of the various isotopes directly to determine their ratios. It is nowadays often possible to dispense completely with chemical analyses of relative or absolute abundance of parent and daughter elements in a radioactive decay series. The technique used is that of isotope dilution, which was originally introduced to geological problems in the rubidium—strontium dating. In this method the sample is mixed with various small amounts of the same element of known isotope ratios. The variations in isotope ratio resulting in the mixture and recorded in the mass spectrometer permit a calculation of the isotopic ratio of the original sample. Samples of elements with uniform isotopic composition are currently produced by atomic reactors, and as such are available for absolute geologic dating.

The use of isotope dilution in mass spectrometry has been a major stride forward in absolute dating. Instead of the clumsy chemical techniques, the quantitative analyses of parent and daughter elements, in which even the smallest samples are composed of a very great number of atoms, we now only need a couple of mass spectrometric analyses. The samples may now be very much smaller than in chemical analysis, because the mass spectrometer counts each atom of the sample. Under ideal circumstances age determinations can now be made on quantities of 1 μg (a microgram, or one millionth of a gram).

Mass spectrometry has consequently made possible the use of the rubidium—strontium and the potassium—argon decay for absolute dating. It also gave a new impetus to the lead method. At present it is possible to measure separately the ^{232}thorium—^{208}lead, the ^{235}uranium—^{207}lead and the ^{238}uranium—^{206}lead amounts in uranium minerals. Moreover, it is possible to check the amount of these three radiogenic isotopes of lead against the non-radiogenic ^{204}lead in the sample. This, however, still asks for chemical assaying of the amounts of thorium, uranium and total lead. But in using so-called lead—lead ages, derived from quotients such as $\dfrac{^{206}\text{Pb}}{^{207}\text{Pb}}$, age determinations can be made in which the total amount of parent element no longer enters.

This is very important, because in this way independent checks can be made of a possible loss of certain elements during the radioactive decay. Both of the uraniums and thorium have gaseous intermediate steps in their decay series, such as radon gas, which can easily escape over geologic periods. Moreover, the 'stable' end, the daughter isotopes of lead, are not very stable in the crust of the earth, but tend to segregate elsewhere through the influence of various processes over the millions of years. The amount of loss of radiogenic lead and other components can be checked by measuring various quotients of the lead isotopes. Only when all values determined by the different lead methods concur, is there a probability that no serious losses of radiogenic products have occurred. In this case, the so-called 'concordant lead age' has proven as reliable a method of dating as those based on the other decay series.

Reliability of absolute dating

To sum up this digression on the methods of absolute age determination, it follows that the techniques have shown a stupendous development over the past decades. Moreover, the scientists engaged in this work nowadays try to date one sample by as many techniques as possible. Because of the very small quantities now required of the actual elements, most rocks, even those containing very minor quantities of these elements, can still be dated by both the potassium—argon and the rubidium—strontium methods, as well as by various lead techniques. Consequently, it is common nowadays to see a single age determination of a given rock sample reported upon by some ten or more authors. Some of these are responsible for the geologic mapping and sampling, others for the chemical preparation, whilst the rest has made the requisite isotope measurements for the various types of age determination. Moreover, there are frequent inter-laboratory checks made on parts of a single rock sample to ensure reproducibility of the measurements.

If we now look at the results, it is quite natural for a person not acquainted with absolute dating to become bewildered by the figures produced. Ages of millions and billions of years are discussed, and if it is natural to distrust such pronouncements and to question their validity, this reserve may have grown because of the many times absolute dates have proved to be erroneous in the past. Moreover, not only have many absolute dates suffered quite considerable corrections, but these have also tended mostly towards older and still older ages. So one quite naturally gained the impression that for every year that these nuclear scientists investigated the age of the earth, this age did rise a couple of million years.

In a sense this development sometimes gave the impression of bluffing, in producing older and older dates. My aim is to show that absolute dating in geology is not bluffing, nor even guesswork any more. It is based not only on a number of sound physical laws, but on several parallel techniques by which the results can be checked independently.

On the other hand, we must admit that these techniques are still difficult to apply. Not only do they ask the utmost of present-day electronic instrumentation, but also the rocks which now form the crust of the earth, which contain the physical clocks used, have, of course, been subjected to all kinds of vicissitudes during the long eras of their history.

However, let us skip these details. In broad outline we may conclude that the absolute dates so far are to be trusted as as near an approximation of the real age of the rocks in question as we may possibly obtain at this moment.

THE LONG EARLY HISTORY OF THE EARTH

As its most general result, absolute dating has made us aware of the extremely long early history of the earth, that part of its history which has been only very meagerly documented. Only when life on earth had developed forms with hard parts, such as skeletons, did abundant fossilisation become possible. This began, more or less simultaneously, in a number of different zoological phylae at the beginning of the Cambrian system. This is the first system of the Paleozoic era, and every geologist working with fossils feels that there is a clean break in the history of the earth at that time. There is the later history of the earth, from the Cambrian system onwards, in which one can nicely date findings with fossils, and then there is that vague, earlier period, almost without fossils, the pre-Cambrian.

This break, occurring at the base of the Cambrian system, has now been dated at about 600 million years ago. But the oldest crustal rock so far for which a radioactive date has been established is 3,300 million years old.

So all the eras of the Paleozoic, the Mesozoic and the Cenozoic together, with their 600 million years' time-span, take up less than one fifth of the time during which our earth had already developed an outer crust more or less similar to the crust we live on now.

It is at some time during this very early period of the earth's history that the origin of life took place.

Tables II and III give a recent geological time-scale (Kulp, 1960) in which this difference between 'normal' and earlier geologic history is well expressed. The first table gives the ages and the duration of the eras and systems since the beginning of the Paleozoic, the time during which fossils were more or less abundant. The second table includes all earlier datings and consequently immediately focusses attention on the long duration of earlier geologic history and on the long duration of the pre-Cambrian.

Figs. 35 and 36 also clearly show this difference. Fig. 35 schematically shows the development of life on earth over the last 600 millions of years. Fig. 36 presents more schematically the distinction between the time of the origin of life on earth, a couple of billion years ago, and its later development since the beginning of the Cambrian system and the Paleozoic era.

TABLE II

TIME SCALE OF 'NORMAL' GEOLOGY: AGE AND DURATION OF ERAS AND
SYSTEMS (OR EPOCHS) SINCE THE BEGINNING OF THE PALEOZOIC
(from Kulp, 1960)

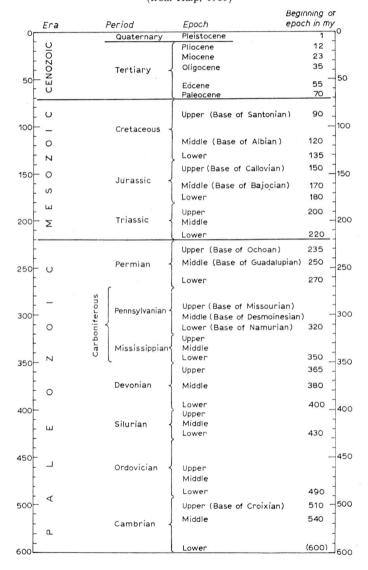

TABLE III

GEOLOGIC TIME SCALE : DATES OF MAIN EVENTS SINCE THE
ORIGIN OF THE EARTH (IN MY)
(from Kulp, 1960)

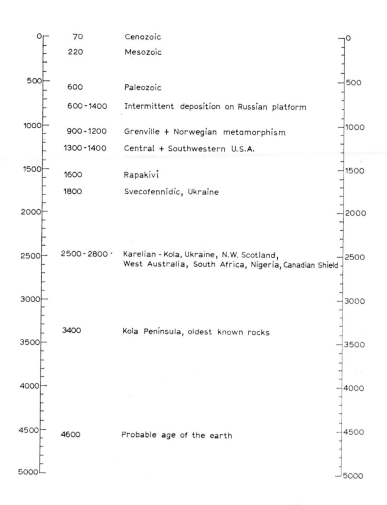

70	Cenozoic	
220	Mesozoic	
600	Paleozoic	
600-1400	Intermittent deposition on Russian platform	
900-1200	Grenville + Norwegian metamorphism	
1300-1400	Central + Southwestern U.S.A.	
1600	Rapakivi	
1800	Svecofennidic, Ukraine	
2500-2800	Karelian - Kola, Ukraine, N.W. Scotland, West Australia, South Africa, Nigeria, Canadian Shield	
3400	Kola Peninsula, oldest known rocks	
4600	Probable age of the earth	

CHAPTER IV

THE BIOLOGICAL APPROACH

In the preceding chapters we have seen how strong uniformitarianism is as a philosophy in geology and how geology accepts extrapolation, in a general way, of actual processes into the geological past, even over time-spans of millions and billions of years. Consequently, we must now first look into the results of biological studies of life at present and their bearing on the origin of life. We must learn what characterizes life at present; what we may call living and what we regard as dead; what actual processes are at work in living things now, or, put in other words, what is the metabolism of the present forms of life.

Biologists interested in the origin of life have supplied us with an outstanding summary of the state of their science — together with some gleanings from astronomy and geology — in the proceedings of the Symposium of the International Union of Biochemistry, held at Moscow in 1957. These proceedings, originally edited by Oparin, Pasynski, Braunshtein and Pavlovskaya later appeared in an English—French—German version, edited by Clark and Synge, as Vol. I of the I.U.B. Symposium Series in 1959 under the title *The Origin of Life on Earth* (Oparin *et al.*, 1959). Later a shorter account appeared, containing selected papers but not the discussions (Florkin (Ed.), 1960), under the title *Aspects of the Origin of Life*. It is from these accounts mainly that the following statements are drawn. They contain a summary of the biological approach to our problem, as far as is necessary to understand its geological aspects.

NON-LIVING AND LIVING IN BIOLOGY

One of the main difficulties biologists have to cope with is the ultimate distinction between living and dead. This difficulty, of course, does not arise so strongly in the more well-known examples of man or the higher organised animals and plants. No doubts are felt about the living or dead in relation, for example, to the obituary column of our daily papers. It is in the so-called lower reaches of living matter, that difficulties arise to distinguish between the living and non-living; between the more lowly, unicellular or non-cellular organisms on the one hand, and big, non-living molecules on the other; between extremely simple systems of metabolism and reproduction which are very similar to chemical reactions, but still belong to living forms, and complicated chemical reactions between very large molecules, which still have to be considered non-living.

In these borderline cases it is impossible to separate by a strict definition the living, not so much from the dead, but from the non-living. For instance, even the fact that all living things contain protein, whilst part of their metabolism is based on a protein cycle, does not enable a watertight definition. It forms, of course, an easy schematization. This property of all living matter to contain protein will be helpful as a tenably descriptive character of life on earth for the geologist, but it does not preclude other possibilities. We can think of possible forms of life not based on protein. Or, much more important, we can imagine protein to be formed in an anorganic mode, if only in circumstances sufficiently different from the present natural environment on earth.

This distinction between the living and non-living, which is so important to biologists, however, requires a knowledge of details much smaller than can ever be solved by the geological record. The geologist never sees the life he describes. He only finds its remnants, not only dead, but fossilized. This means that even the material of the former living organism is replaced by 'stone' or by minerals. When this replacement has proceeded along orderly lines, molecule by molecule, structure can be preserved in its minutest microscopic detail. This is the best the geologist can hope for generally, whereas actual preservation of organic substance is rare in the extreme.

Of course, the biologist, the biochemist in particular, normally also uses sections from dead organisms, dead cells, or even extracts from cells expressly broken up by laboratory techniques. Using dead remains to study life, he is, in a way, like a drunk who has lost his key in the dark before the door but is looking for it under the lamp-post, because he can see better there (Winkler, 1960). But although he also uses dead remains to study life, he himself has killed the living organisms only a couple of moments before, by techniques known to him and selected to provide the least distorted picture.

NON-LIVING AND LIVING IN GEOLOGY

The tools of geology, this must be stated quite clearly, are so much coarser that for us this distinction between living and non-living is not a practical question at all. The best we can hope for is to find fossilized remains of organisms which formerly lived on earth. Only very rarely do we have some idea of how these forms died — for instance, when they were buried by volcanic ash, or slid into an asphalt pool. Moreover, apart from the fact that we generally do not know how our fossils-to-be died, we also have only the vaguest ideas of why and how they were preserved, and how and when the fossilization process, the replacement of the original organic material by mineral matter, took place. Apart from the fossilized remains themselves, we can study, as a further indication, the environment in which these remains were buried in the rock and from these make a considered guess about the environment in which the organism that later became preserved as a fossil, had lived.

To be at all recognisable as remnants of former living organisms, fossils must have preserved some clearly organized shape or structure, recognizable as such by the eye, by a hand lens or by with the aid of a normal microscope. These remains of former living organisms, preserved from the geologic past, are not merely dead, but long since dead and fossilized. They can no more yield the fresh preparations biologists study under the electron microscope or the extracts they prepare in an ultracentrifuge. Our remains, let it be stated again, are dead and fossilized.

Organisms capable of being detected in a fossilized state by a geologist after billions of years may well belong to the 'lower' organisms, to unicellular forms as bacteria or certain algae; in short, to microbes. But the organization of such forms has progressed already a long way from that borderland between living and non-living the biologist is interested in. Fossilized remains from the early history of life must already show some cellular structure. There is little doubt these remains are from organisms fully alive, and not from some borderland proto-life.

CHEMICAL UNIFORMITY OF PRESENT MODE OF LIFE

Returning now to the biological studies of present life, we find as a salient feature of modern life the antithesis between the immense variation of its morphological expression and the small number of chemical reactions on which it is based. Morphologically, there is an enormous number of different forms of life, species, genera, families and higher systematic realms of microbes, plants and animals. Estimates run to about one million different species existing on earth today. Biochemically, in contrast, all present-day life, in all its variations, is based on nucleic acids, proteins, carbohydrates and fats and some minor compounds such as phosphoric esters. Although showing great variation in detail, these compounds are all interrelated and built upon a few scores only of basic biochemical reactions. Marine animals and plants, from the smallest species of plankton drifting in the currents, to huge whales, or continental plants and animals, from the viruses to the elephants, aerobic or anaerobic organisms, all are based on this surprisingly small number of organic compounds.

Nature, it has been said, is so organized that any living thing forms part of the food chain, can be fed on by other living things. Owing to the small number of organic compounds used in building up any form of life, there is always, in any organism, something digestible for some other organism. Scientists are amused by this. They interpret the biochemical similarity as an indication that all present forms of life are related somehow, and consequently that all forms of life have a common origin.

The chemical compounds which build up all living forms today, together form the compounds of natural organic chemistry, as opposed to inorganic chemistry. They form only a very small part, however, of the organic compounds which it is possible to synthesize from these same elements. Or, to use teleological jargon, Nature was extremely narrow-minded in her chemical conceptions. Every chemist today can make a much greater number and variety of organic compounds, than Nature formed in a couple of billion years.

If we now look more closely into this group of natural organic compounds, proteins, carbohydrates, fats and some others, we find that they are formed mainly from the elements C, O, H and N. Several of these compounds, particularly the proteins, form very large molecules of an intricate structure. The structure of these large organic molecules is now in the process of being unravelled, and papers relating to this study are common in scientific and popular literature. We need not go into this matter here, if we only retain from these biological studies of our present life the fact that most natural organic compounds are formed by large and complicated molecules.

IMPOSSIBILITY OF NATURAL SYNTHESIS OF ORGANIC COMPOUNDS IN THE PRESENT ATMOSPHERE

This fact is of decisive importance for an evaluation of the possibilities of the origin of life, for the synthesis by natural inorganic processes of such large, complicated molecules happens to be wellnigh impossible under present environmental circumstances. Under our present conditions of temperature, light, composition of the atmosphere and the hydrosphere, only much smaller molecules formed from the same elements are stable, whilst the larger organic compounds are unstable. Even if, by some extremely unlikely coincidence, such an organic molecule had formed, it would be destroyed again immediately, either by inorganic oxidation processes, or by organic oxidation, such as rotting. So these large organic molecules cannot at present exist on their own, inorganically, without any relation whatsoever to living organisms. They cannot be formed regularly, or even rarely, in natural inorganic chemistry and even if this would be possible, they are liable to immediate destruction.

The statements above do, of course, no more than paraphrase the wide gulf that at present exists in nature between organic and inorganic chemical compounds, — a gulf so wide that until it had been bridged by the synthesis of ureum in 1828, it seemed as if even man-made chemistry would forever be unable to produce these organic molecules, a process which seemed reserved exclusively to the metabolism of living things.

So we must realise that natural organic compounds cannot, by any means, be formed in nature now, except through processes occurring in living matter already in existence. Under present conditions, it follows that the origin of life from inorganic beginnings is impossible, because only living matter in its turn can synthesize organic compounds. Only living matter can produce other living matter.

THE OXYGENIC ATMOSPHERE OF THE PRESENT

The crucial point lies not, however, in the fact that such an origin is altogether impossible, but only in that it is impossible under present circumstances. The most essential of these is that present environmental conditions for life on earth are all based on the fact that our present atmosphere contains an appreciable amount of free oxygen.

The free oxygen of our atmosphere, and the free oxygen dissolved in most of our hydrosphere, enables the breathing by most plants and animals. This is the most important part of their energy cycle, and as such forms the basis for poetic quotations about the 'life-giving' oxygen. There is, however, another important aspect to this free atmospheric oxygen. An aspect much less easily perceptible in our every day life than breathing, but still of equal, or even higher importance. This is that the free oxygen in the higher reaches of the atmosphere forms a relatively thin layer of ozone. Ozone absorbs most of the ultraviolet light emitted by the sun and consequently shields us from these rays. A small amount of the longer ultraviolet rays can be sustained, and may even produce a healthy sunburn, but the full spectrum of the ultraviolet rays, in the intensity as produced by the sun, is more deadly to present-day life on earth than any radiation due to radioactive decay.

Of the two effects of free atmospheric oxygen, the possibility of the breathing and shielding from the ultraviolet rays, the second only is a *conditio sine qua non* for the present life on earth. We know a wide variety of anaerobic microbes, which have quite a variation of metabolism cycles, in which free oxygen plays no part. Free oxygen is even deadly to most of them, and because our atmosphere contains free oxygen in large quantities, these forms can only live when shut off from the atmosphere so well that they are able to reduce small amounts of oxygen reaching them. So there is at present life on earth which lives and propagates under the exclusion of free oxygen.

However, both aerobic and anaerobic forms would be killed off by the shorter ultraviolet sunrays if these were not filtered out high up in the atmosphere by the ozone layer. This in turn depends on the presence of free oxygen in our atmosphere. Therefore, in the absence of free atmospheric oxygen, even the anaerobic life we now know would have difficulty in surviving, not because its metabolic processes would not be adapted to suit that atmosphere, but because it would be killed off by the ultraviolet sunrays directly reaching the surface of the earth. Only if shielded by water or soil, in lakes and oceans, or in pores in the soil, would there be a chance for early life similar to our present anaerobic microbes to service in such an environment.

ANOXYGENIC PRIMEVAL ATMOSPHERE

All present-day theories about a natural origin of life on earth, theories which all go back to the original ideas of Oparin, all postulate an early or primeval atmosphere of reducing character, in which there is no free oxygen.

Oxygen will have been present at that time only in chemical compounds, of which water will have been the most important. Apart from water, this early atmosphere, and also, of course, the early hydrosphere, the contemporaneous rivers, lakes and oceans, will also have carried carbon and nitrogen, mostly in compounds also, and a host of other elements. Amongst these sulphur and phosphorus may have been the most important as catalysts in early energy cycles. The difference with our present atmosphere lies in the fact that there could not have been present, in that primeval atmosphere, an appreciable amount of free oxygen.

Views on the relative abundance of the elements and their compounds in that early atmosphere and hydrosphere vary with different authors. The mixture of water with these compounds in the early hydrosphere is often referred to as the 'thin soup', which obviates the necessity of making too strict an estimate of its composition.

INORGANIC SYNTHESIS OF 'ORGANIC' COMPOUNDS IN PRIMEVAL ATMOSPHERE

The important thing is not the exact composition of the primeval atmosphere and hydrosphere. The important thing is the absence of free oxygen and the presence, consequently, of relatively simple compounds of the elements C, O, H, N, S and P, which nowadays occur exclusively as natural organic compounds, accompanying compounds like CO_2, H_2O, SiO_2, silicates, sulphates and the like which now also belong to natural inorganic chemistry.

The possible presence of these compounds is a direct result, in a twofold way, of the existence of a primeval atmosphere without free oxygen. First, in such an atmosphere these compounds, which at present can only be formed in a natural way through the metabolism of living matter, can be built by processes of inorganic chemistry. And not only can they be built up regularly in such an atmosphere, but they are also stable, or at least so stable that they are not destroyed at a rate comparable to that of their formation. This is also due to the reducing character of an atmosphere without free oxygen, in which the present-day oxidizing and decomposition processes do not occur.

But let us first look further into the reason why in such a primeval atmosphere, which is anoxygenic, *i.e.* without free oxygen, there is a possibility that simple 'organic' compounds are formed by way of natural inorganic chemistry. This possibility is the direct result of the absence of a shielding layer of ozone, developed from the free oxygen in the higher atmosphere. Ultraviolet sunlight of shorter wavelengths is then not filtered out by the ozone, and can freely reach the surface of the earth. Light of such short wavelength is of very high energy. One result would be, as we have seen, that present-day life would be killed off by such high-energy radiation. Another result, however, would be that this same high energy permits inorganic photochemical reactions at the surface of the earth which do not occur now, because that part of the sunlight which gets through the ozone layer does not have a high enough energy. The shorter ultraviolet radiation of the sun is, in fact, so rich in energy that it may excite several elements of the 'thin soup' to form chemical bonds; in other words, to form molecular compounds through the adsorption of light quanta. This is a thoroughly inorganic process, yet under the circumstances it may produce typically 'organic' molecules, up to and including amino-acids.

The process is dependent upon the absorption of light quanta from the shorter ultraviolet rays: it is photosynthesis. But it is inorganic photosynthesis. It must not be confused with the organic photosynthesis which takes place at present in plants through catalytic action of porphyrins or chlorophyll, and mainly using light quanta from the red part of the sunlight.

GENERATIO SPONTANEA

In literature, this inorganic photosynthesis of 'organic' compounds is sometimes called *generatio spontanea*. *Generatio spontanea* has, however, for a long time been a sort of catch-all for a mode of origin of life on earth which was not understood, which it was not possible to study, or which was something akin to, or just the opposite of, creation. At present, now that the possible modes of origin of life

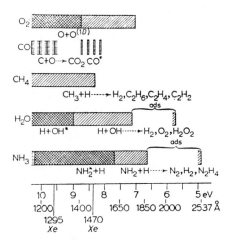

Fig. 8. Spectral ranges of photochemical sensitivity for gases (from A. N. Terenin, 1959). Oxygen is seen to absorb the ultraviolet light from a wavelength of 1850 Å downwards. The energy values of the corresponding light quanta, expressed in electronvolts, is seen to rise from about 7 eV for light of 1800 Å to 10 eV for light of 1200 Å. In this region the other gases mentioned are photochemically active, as is indicated by the hatching and cross-hatching. The asterisks indicate at what wavelength the radicals in question start emitting light, a phenomenon without significance for the synthesis of larger molecules, but important for their recognition during the experiment. The dashed arrows indicate the spectral ranges at which composite molecules, formed from atoms and radicals are built up. The two Xenon lines of 1295 Å and 1470 Å indicate the strong monochromatic radiation of the xenon lamp, which Groth used as early as 1938 in experiments of this kind.

on earth through natural causes form the subject of intense scientific studies, it seems better to drop altogether the term of *generatio spontanea.*

EXPERIMENTAL CHECKS

The theoretical importance of the shorter ultraviolet rays of the sunlight, those with a wavelength below 1850 Å, for photosynthetic inorganic processes from simple stable gases such as CO, CH_4, H_2O and NH_3, is illustrated in Fig. 8, taken from the recent review of Terenin (1959). The result of experimental studies of the regions of adsorption, at which photochemical activity may take place of just those gases from which a primeval atmosphere might be formed, and which would form the buildingstones of any primary 'organic' molecules, show that these coincide with that of free oxygen, its dissociation products and ozone. Consequently, the present atmosphere is opaque to light of such short wavelengths, which is absorbed by the ozone high up in the atmosphere. Hydrogen, on the other hand, is quite transparent for light of this wavelength. So in an atmosphere composed principally of hydrogen, these rays of sunlight

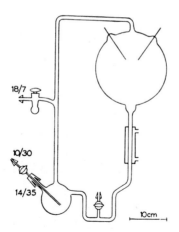

Fig. 9. Diagram of spark-discharge apparatus, used to produce 'organic' compounds from hydrogen, methane, ammonia and water in an anoxygenic environment (from S. L. Miller, 1959).

could penetrate through the atmosphere to the surface of the earth.

This is no mere theoretical possibility: experiments have in later years proved that mixtures of gases such as given in Fig. 8 can yield many different 'organic' compounds when treated with water in glass vessels by strong electrical sparks or by irradiation with short ultra-violet rays, the only pre-requisite being the absence of free oxygen. The best known experiments are those by Miller (1959, 1960), who succeeded in producing amino-acids in this way. Moreover, Wilson (1960) recently reported how even far larger molecules could be formed under similar conditions.

A schematized drawing of the spark discharge apparatus used by Miller is given in Fig. 9. Electrical sparks are used for convenience. Their energy is smaller than can be obtained by irradiation with shorter ultraviolet light, but they present fewer experimental difficulties. The small flask in the lower left-hand corner contains water, whilst the rest of the system contains, say, a mixture of hydrogen, methane and ammonia. The water is boiled, the spark is operated

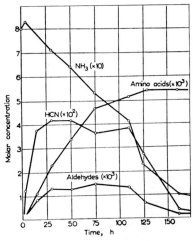

Fig. 10. Concentrations of ammonia, hydrogen cyanide and aldehydes in the U-tube, and amino-acids in the 500 ml flask, while sparking a mixture of methane, ammonia, water and hydrogen in the apparatus of Fig. 9 (from S. L. Miller, 1959).

continuously, and through the U-tube the non-volatile compounds accumulate in the small flask. The result of a typical run is given in Fig. 10. During the first 25 hours mainly hydrogen cyanide and aldehydes form at the expense of ammonia. Their concentration then becomes stabilized, whilst the formation of amino-acids proceeds regularly up to about 125 hours, still at the expense of the original ammonia.

Wilson (1960) recently succeeded in producing much larger polymeric molecules, each built up by 20 carbon atoms and more. These formed sheetlike solids, in the spark-discharge flask, of the order of 1 cm across. It is thought that in this case surface-active molecules were formed, which built up films on the gas—liquid surfaces. This agrees well with the general idea that films of sheet-like molecules (Figs. 11-13), forming either on the gas—liquid, the gas—solid or the liquid—solid interfaces, must have been extremely important in the early stages of the inorganic processes which eventually led up to the earliest life.

Fig. 11. Sheet-like films of 'organic' macromolecules, produced by sparking a mixture of water, ammonia, hydrogen sulphide and ashes of baker's yeast (from A. T. Wilson, 1960).

Fig. 12. Electron microphotograph of sheet-like, 'organic' macromolecules, produced by sparking a mixture theoretically comparable to the primeval hydrosphere (from A. T. Wilson, 1960) (magnification x 6500).

Fig. 13. Electron microphotograph of a single 'organic' macromolecule (see Fig. 12) (magnification x 16120).

Fig. 11.

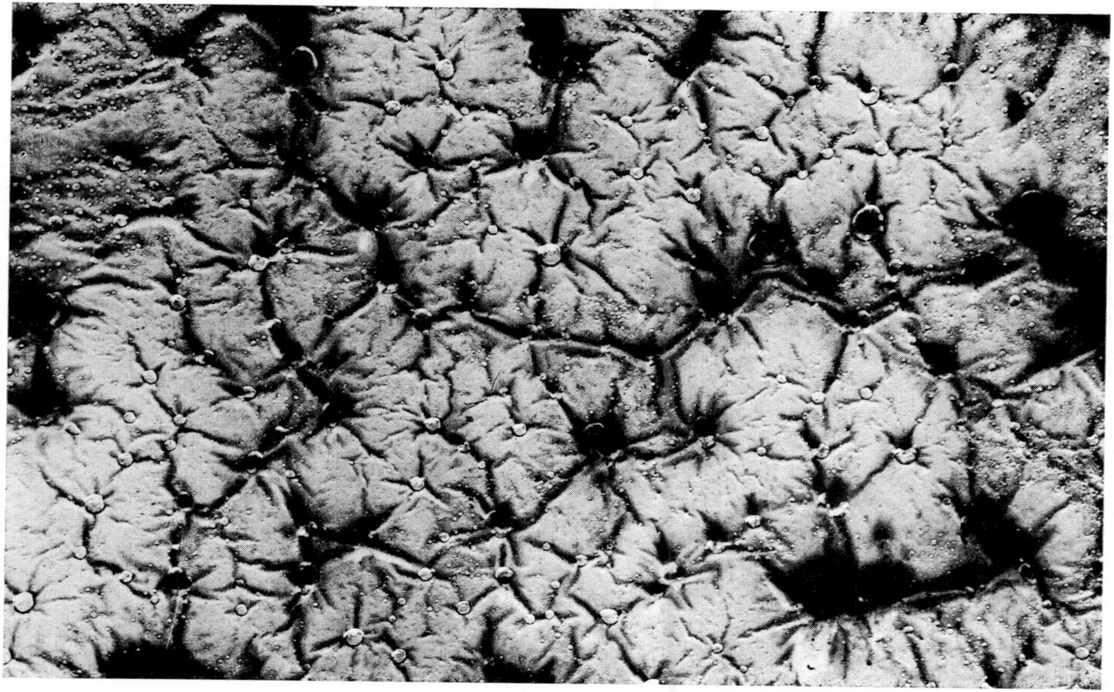

Fig. 12.

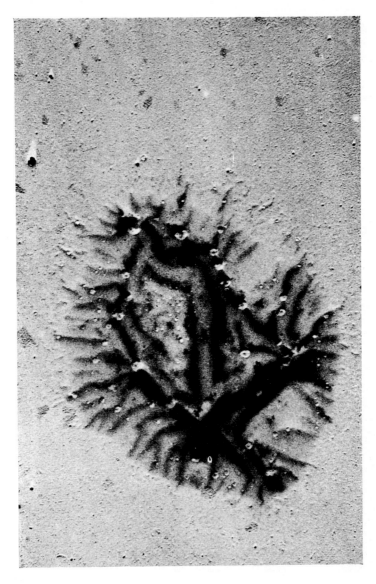

Fig. 13.

Many other elements must have taken part in these early processes of inorganic photosynthesis. In contrast to the present life, with its extremely varied morphological expression based on a narrowly limited number of biochemical reactions, these early processes of inorganic photosynthesis, this proto-life, probably showed very large chemical variety, but was probably not yet coupled to any definite morphology.

Pirie stressed this difference in his famous drawing, which is reproduced here as Fig. 14. In an extremely simplified form, the evolu-

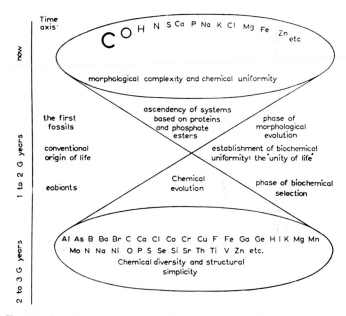

Fig. 14. Simplified presentation of the origin and the development of life on earth, according to Pirie (1959). The lower cone shows the early inorganic chemical processes and the early life, chemically diversified but without much morphological expression. The upper cone represents the development of our present mode of life, characterized by morphological diversification upon a narrowly restricted group of biochemical reactions.

tion of life can be represented by a double cone. The lower one symbolizes the early mode, of life with its great number of elements participating in inorganic photosynthetic and allied processes in the primeval atmosphere without free oxygen. The upper cone represents the development of present life, with a strong morphological variation based on a certain group of narrowly limited biochemical reactions under the new oxygenic atmosphere.

From the first inorganic photosynthetic reactions occurring under the primeval atmosphere, which led to the formation of the 'thin soup', an extremely long time elapsed before the appearance of anything resembling living matter: a stretch of time filled, of course, with an extremely large number of different activities. An exact limit is difficult to draw. It is, perhaps, even irrelevant. It is less important where to draw the dividing line between non-living and living, than to retain the fundamental much more important difference existing between the primeval and the new atmosphere, and, moreover, to note that, as we will see, real life existed already in that primeval atmosphere, life that was capable of producing if not fossils, at least remains recognizable as organic products. Real life co-existed with proto-life, and also with those photosynthetic reactions which one should like to call inorganic by all means. Although still anoxygenic in metabolism, it was a form of real life co-existing with the earlier forms, with the eobionts of Pirie.

In general, there will have been an early evolution towards bigger and more complicated molecules of 'organic' substances still formed by inorganic processes. These bigger molecules were normally built up by smaller units, each of similar structure. They are repetitive and consist of chains of identical or related blocks. Such molecules, however, through small physico-chemical differences with comparable compounds in their surroundings, are often able to incorporate new blocks into their structure; or, in other words, to grow.

Such growing will have been favoured, for certain kinds of compounds, by the nature of their substratum; for instance, by adsorption on clays or quartz, then as now, probably the two most common minerals of the surface of the earth. At that time sulphides, too, will have been abundant, for instance, in the form of pyrite sands. Sulphur is known for its strong catalytic properties in reactions such as those under discussion. It is, for example, noteworthy that Wilson in his experiments succeeded in producing macromolecules after introducing H_2S into his mixture. So the presence of sulphur might have been an important factor in those early days.

A further step will have been that various kinds of these bigger, 'growing' molecules became dominant. From this stage to life-like compounds with specific metabolistic processes and capable of propagation, is, of course, another step requiring a great number of separate reactions. However, it is a step which, although taken in a gradual way by a large number of separate reactions, is quite well conceivable from our present knowledge of both inorganic and organic chemistry.

MUTANTS ACQUIRING A NEW SKILL: ORGANIC PHOTOSYNTHESIS

Life in that early time, still under the primeval atmosphere, even then must have produced mutants. For mutation is something akin to those larger molecules of 'organic' composition. Although still not well understood, mutation is the result of some minor switch-over in local structure of one of the small building blocks of a large molecule; a switch-over due to some energy flux, probably mostly external, which might be of thermal or radiative character.

Somewhere, sometime, mutations of that early life will have produced compounds capable of organic photosynthesis, *i.e.* of organic assimilation. They acquired the unique capability of dissociating carbon dioxide (CO_2) into carbon (C) and free oxygen (O_2). The carbon may be used to build more organic matter for the living organism, whilst the oxygen escapes into the atmosphere.

The results of this new capability of early life have been complex, and in the end overwhelming. The first benefit of organic photosynthesis was not so much in the easy acquisition of carbon to build more living matter, but in the much greater energy freed by this process, when compared to the anaerobic metabolism. Any such reactions in which free oxygen is not involved, such as those of nitrate-, sulphate- or carbonate-reducing bacteria, have a much lower energy production than freed by the assimilation of carbon dioxide. The new way of life consequently gave an immediate advantage in the struggle for life over those contemporary organisms which were still based on earlier metabolism.

However, another, still more important change will have domi-
nated gradually. Through the organic photosynthesis, through the
assimilation of carbon dioxide, free oxygen will have become a more
and more important part of the atmosphere. It is postulated that all
free oxygen present now in the atmosphere has been formed through
organic photosynthesis. All of our free oxygen thus is biogenic in
origin. This oxygen will have gradually shielded the surface of the
earth from the shorter ultraviolet rays of the sunlight, and an environment comparable to our present one will have been realized
step by step. This in turn will finally have led to the extinction of
all earlier processes of life or life-like reactions which were possible
in the primeval atmosphere by utilisation of the energy of the shorter
ultraviolet radiation from the sun.

GRADUAL TRANSITION FROM PRIMEVAL TO PRESENT ATMOSPHERE

This transition from the primeval anoxygenic, reducing atmosphere
to the present oxidizing one consequently was one of the prime events
in the history of our earth. One is tempted to describe this transition
as catastrophic. All earlier life was doomed to extinction, and all
later life, up to that of the present, found its origin at that period.
But, as we have seen in the preceding chapters, even such a 'catastrophic' event will have taken its time. It will have occurred very
gradually, not only according to human perception of time, but even
geologically speaking. The production of free oxygen through organic
assimilation was, of course, a slow process. It will have taken quite
a long time before free oxygen had been produced in such quantities
that a layer of ozone was developed in the higher atmosphere to be
capable of effective absorption of the shorter ultraviolet sunlight.

So, because the change over from the primeval atmosphere to our
present one, although catastrophic in its ultimate results, was a
gradual process, both the earlier chemical inorganic reactions producing 'organic' material, and the earlier forms of life based on
anoxygenic metabolism, and the new life capable of organic photosynthesis, of assimilation of carbon dioxyde, must have been co-
existent on earth for a long time; probably for millions of years. The
point of intersection between the two cones in the famous Pirie
drawing (Fig. 14), will in reality have formed an extensive area
in time.

THE ASTRONOMER'S VIEW

Before finishing this chapter, we may well look into one other aspect of the origin of life on earth, although it is not biological. This is the astronomical viewpoint. A short review can, indeed, be added here, because astronomers and biologists are very much in agreement on this matter. Both in the complete volume on the Moscow Symposium of the I.U.B., and in Florkin (1960), several papers on the astronomical aspects have appeared. The main result is that at present various cosmological theories exist, starting either from an original 'hot earth' or from an original 'cold earth'. Both are, however, compatible with modern biological views on the origin of life on earth through natural causes. This follows from the fact that, astronomically speaking, the earth was well finished before the possibility arose for an origin of life.

There is, however, one interesting point here, in relation to the free oxygen of our atmosphere. According to astronomers, our earth is too small, it lacks enough mass and consequently has not the requisite force of gravity, to retain permanently free oxygen. A planet like ours ought not to have any appreciable free oxygen in its atmosphere, because, even if it had been there originally, the escape rate from the higher parts of the atmosphere into interstellar space is far too high. Only through a process resembling, for example, the organic assimilation of carbon dioxide, by which free oxygen is constantly released into the atsmosphere, is an oxygenic atmosphere to be expected. Consequently, astronomers are agreeable to the supposition that all free oxygen in our atmosphere at present is of biogenetic origin, formed through assimilation in plants, by dissociation of carbon dioxide.

Chapter V

THE TWO ATMOSPHERES: ANOXYGENIC AND OXYGENIC, PRE-ACTUALISTIC AND ACTUALISTIC

AEROBIC AND ANAEROBIC, OXYGENIC AND ANOXYGENIC

The difference between the primeval anoxygenic atmosphere and the present oxygenic one is as clear-cut as between black and white. Admittedly, there will have been a long period of transition. But before that time, and after that time, there is complete antithesis between the two.

In the literature, this difference has not always been sufficiently stressed. For one thing, most authors speak of 'anaerobic' conditions prevailing in the primeval atmosphere. This results from the fact that our present anaerobic life forms live under conditions which, in a superficial way, are comparable biochemically. That is, they live under the exclusion of free oxygen. But this is at present an exceptional environmental niche, depending on the exclusion of air, of the atmosphere, which now contains free oxygen. Hence they are properly named 'anaerobic'.

Life in the primeval atmosphere and in the contemporary hydrosphere was, however, far from anaerobic, although the absence of free oxygen led to a superficial biochemical resemblance. Life was indeed aerobic; it could follow its functions in the free atmosphere; it was exposed to the air. But, the atmosphere at that time did not contain free oxygen.

Although life in the primeval atmosphere will have been largely aerobic, just as it is now, this does not, of course, alter the fact that aerobic in the primeval atmosphere was diametrically opposed to what the aerobic environment is now. Consequently, one had better speak of the early anoxygenic atmosphere, of anoxygenic aerobic life under the primeval atmosphere, as opposed to the oxygenic aerobic life of today.

ARADIATIC FOR SHORTER ULTRAVIOLET LIGHT

Moreover, there is, at present, our anaerobic life, which is also an-oxygenic. We do not yet know whether, in the anoxygenic period, there was also anaerobic (and anoxygenic) life, similarly excluded from the primeval atmosphere. There is, however, a probability that the early life forms which developed organic photosynthesis and assimilation, were under disadvantages more or less comparable to those anaerobic life is exposed to at present.

Organic assimilation will then probably have been based on pro-tein, as it is now. Proteins, however, now are non-resistant to radia-tion of the shorter ultraviolet light, which then still reached the surface of the earth. Hence it is quite possible that the early forms of present-day life, the early ancestors of the group that later took full ascendancy, were limited at the beginning to a set of very narrow environmental conditions, comparable in a sense to the restrictions imposed upon our present-day anaerobic life. They were, of course, not anaerobic, because the atmosphere as such was not harmful at the time. They might, however, well have been aradiatic for the shorter ultraviolet light, if it is permissible to introduce this term. They may have been limited at first to the hydrosphere, living in rivers, lakes or oceans at such a depth that the 'thin soup' had filtered out the obnoxious shorter ultraviolet light, whereas the red part of the spectrum, penetrating much farther and so important to organic photosynthesis, was still available to them. Again, they might have lived in pores in the soil, in free communication with fresh air, but shielded from direct sunlight. Of course, such considerations are quite hypothetic, but knowing the prolific variation life is capable of attaining, it is quite possible that some of the earliest forms capable of organic photosynthesis and being aradiatic for the shorter ultra-violet light, lived in the early hydrosphere, and others in pores of the soil.

PRE-ACTUALISTIC AND ACTUALISTIC

The difference between the two atmospheres lies not only in having or not having free oxygen, but also, as a direct consequence, in whether the shorter ultraviolet light is kept from reaching the surface of the earth, or not. Taken together, I think that these differences between the primeval atmosphere and the present one are so im-

portant that one is justified to designate the primeval atmosphere as
pre-actualistic, in contrast to the present, actualistic one.

I realise this is an equivocal step. Even in the primeval atmosphere, natural processes followed the same laws of nature as they do
now. So there is, if you like, still uniformitarianism. Uniformitarianism even forms the base for all biochemical theory referred to in the
preceding chapter. Chemical bonds in the 'thin soup' are postulated
as having been exactly the same as chemical bonds between the same
compounds found now, either in organisms, or produced in the
laboratory.

However, even if there was this basic sort of uniformitarianism, or
let us say, even if there was a uniformity of processes on the physico-
chemical level, the result is different. The result of these selfsame
processes then and now was often exactly opposite. This difference
follows, let it be stated again, from the complete antithesis between
the primeval anoxygenic atmosphere and the present oxygenic one.

To pin down this distinction, a distinction which is not essential
in its underlying primary physico-chemical processes, but which is so
very fundamental in its ultimate result as revealed in the environment eventually created on the surface of the earth, one is justified,
in my opinion, to speak of the difference between primeval and
present atmosphere as pre-actualistic opposed to actualistic.

EXOGENIC AND ENDOGENIC PROCESSES

This distinction between the pre-actualistic anoxygenic atmosphere
and the actualistic oxygenic, of course, also affected the lifeless surface of the earth, the upper layers of the hydrosphere and the lithosphere; that is, all contemporary land surfaces and bodies of water
which stand in close contact with the atmosphere.

In geology, processes which take place on the surface of the land,
on the so-called lithosphere, or in water, in the hydrosphere, together
are grouped as the exogenic processes. They only affect the outer
skin of the earth, and in turn, they are very much affected by the
atmosphere. The group of exogenic processes is different from those
processes occurring within the crust of the earth, which together are
called the endogenic processes. Typical endogenic processes are, for
instance, mountain-building, metamorphosis of rocks at depth, or the
formation of granites, and even, although its products reach the sur-

face, volcanism. Typical exogenic processes are weathering, erosion, soil formation, transportation by rivers and sedimentation in lowlands and oceans.

Now we may state that, in a general way, all exogenic processes are influenced by the composition of the contemporary atmosphere. The proposed usage of the terms pre-actualistic and actualistic thus can be extended from the atmosphere to all contemporary exogenic processes.

The distinction between primeval, anoxygenic and pre-actualistic atmosphere and a later oxygenic and actualistic atmosphere must not, however, be applied to the contemporary endogenic processes. Neither mountain-building nor the formation of a granite batholite, for instance, are influenced by the composition of the atmosphere. This is not a theoretical consideration only. For instance, mountain-building, one of the main endogenic processes, in younger geological periods always seems to follow a certain set pattern of events. In this pattern first very thick sediments are laid down in a definite basin, in which the crust slowly subsides; the so-called geosyncline. Thereupon follows the folding of these sediments, and finally the subsequent crustal rising which, in fact, forms the real mountains. This sequence, called the orogenetic cycle, is the main theme, for instance, of Umbgrove's pulse of the earth (p. 12). Similar sequences, orogenetic cycles which, as far as we are able to study them in the present state of the art of geology, are identical in their main succession to those of younger geologic history, occur far back in the history of the earth. They are found way back to the oldest crustal rocks dated as yet. In contrast to the difference postulated between the early and the present atmosphere and contemporary exogenic processes, there is no such fundamental difference in the endogenic processes. As far back as we can see, endogenic crustal processes have been quite comparable to those found in the younger geologic history. Endogenic processes, for all we know, are actualistic as far back as the oldest rocks dated.

ACTUALISM IN EARLY EXOGENIC AND ENDOGENIC PROCESSES

We will see further on that the transition from the primeval pre-actualistic atmosphere to the present actualistic one may be provisionally dated as having occurred between 2 billion and 1 billion years ago. Endogenic processes, *e.g.* orogenetic cycles, on the other hand, were essentially the same for the oldest rocks dated at the time when this text was written; that is, 3.3 billion years ago.

There is, consequently, a marked difference in the history of the development of endogenic and exogenic processes. At a time when the endogenic processes followed already an actualistic pattern, the latter were still under the influence of the pre-actualistic atmosphere, and completely different from the exogenic processes of younger geologic history and of the present.

CHAPTER VI

WHERE TO LOOK FOR REMAINS OF EARLY LIFE: THE OLD SHIELDS

PAUCITY OF EARLY RECORDS

If we now turn again to geology in our search for facts about the origin of life, we find them deplorably scarce. There are very few fossil finds from the early history of the earth.

This is so for a variety of reasons, which can be summarized as follows: small size and softness of early forms of life, whilst most of the old rocks are masked by younger ones. Also, great age has destroyed many primary structures of the rocks formed at those times.

All early life forms were small, consisting of protoplasm or similar soft tissue, and without hard parts. In the next chapter we will go further into this. Let us only bear in mind here, that the early forms of life are comparable to our microbes, and microbes in general stand an extremely slim chance of becoming fossilized.

Moreover, most of the rocks formed in those early days are not visible for inspection now. They have been buried by thick piles of younger rocks, mostly sediments, and are now situated at depths of several kilometers or even several tens of kilometers. Even where they are again exposed at the surface of the earth, they have often suffered considerable damage during their billion-year history.

They also, although now exposed at the surface, have in most cases been temporarily buried by younger sediments, which have since been removed again. They have often been folded, or intruded by large batholites of granite. All such mishaps expose the rocks to a temporarily elevated temperature or pressure, or both. Through this the minerals which consitute the rock tend to become mobile. They will recombine and recrystallize either into larger crystals of similar composition, or even into crystals of quite different composi-

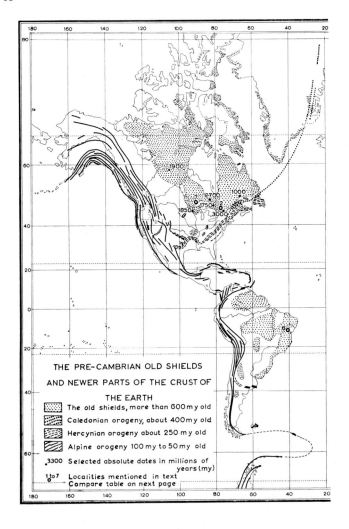

THE PRE-CAMBRIAN OLD SHIELDS
AND NEWER PARTS OF THE CRUST OF
THE EARTH

The old shields, more than 600 m y old
Caledonian orogeny, about 400 m y old
Hercynian orogeny about 250 m y old
Alpine orogeny 100 m y to 50 m y old

.3300 Selected absolute dates in millions of
years (my)

1 to 7 Localities mentioned in text
Compare table on next page

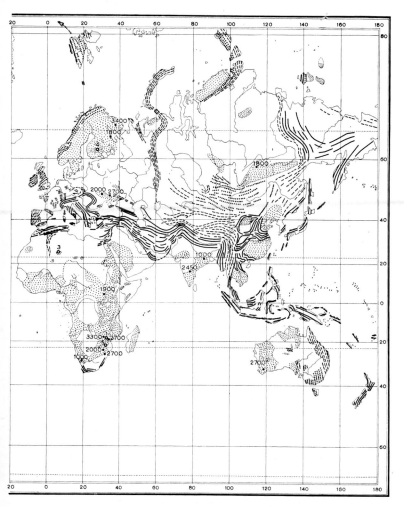

Fig. 15. The pre-Cambrian old shields and newer parts of the crust (from Umbgrove, 1947). Absolute datings mainly from Tilton and Davis, 1959.

TABLE IV

1. Oldest known biogenic deposists, the lime-secreting organisms described by MacGregor. Compare p. 77-82.

2. Oldest known fossils. Primitive plants and microbes, described by Tyler and Barghoorn. Compare p. 83-88.
   Also, in the same general area, Blind River uranium deposits, formed under pre-actualistic atmosphere. Compare p. 99-109.

3. Lime-secreting Algae, related to *Collenia,* described by Gravelle and Lelubre. Compare p. 89-92.

4. Non-oxidized weathering residue of pre-Cambrian granite, formed under pre-actualistic atmosphere, described by Rankama. Compare p. 97, 98.

5. Gold—uranium Dominion Reef and also Witwatersrand reefs, formed under pre-actualistic atmosphere, described by Ramdohr. Compare p. 99-109.

6. Serra de Jacobina gold—uranium reefs, also formed under pre-actualistic atmosphere, described by Ramdohr. Compare p. 99-109.

7. Lake Superior iron ores, at least partly formed under pre-actualistic atmosphere, according to Lepp and Goldich. Compare p. 109, 110.

tion. In either case primary rock structures, such as fossils, will be destroyed.

Although fossil remains are scarce for the early history of life on earth, we must, of course, use what is available. The first point, treated in this chapter is where to look for vestiges of the oldest life on earth. In the next chapter the fossils found will be described, whilst in Chapter VIII the environment of the early life will be studied. This is possible because, as we have seen in the preceding chapter, the environment is mainly controlled by the existence of either a pre-actualistic or an actualistic atmosphere, which in turn influences all contemporary exogenic processes on the surface of the earth.

THE OLD SHIELDS

The fossil remains of early life must be sought for in the oldest areas of the crust of the earth; that is, in the regions technically known as the 'old shields'. These are characterized by pre-Cambrian rocks outcropping at the surface of the earth, without a cover of younger rocks.

In most textbooks of geology the old shields are indicated as quite distinct from the newer regions of the earth's crust. If we look, for instance, at Plate V of Umbgrove's *Pulse of the Earth,* which is redrawn here in Fig. 15, we find the old shields indicated by stippling, without any indication of pronounced structural directions. This is in marked contrast to the newer regions of the crust, where the main directions of younger orogenetic fold belts are indicated.

This difference, suggested in most geology textbooks, between the old shields and the younger areas of the crust, is but an apparent one. It is brought about by the apparent break in classical geology between all of the pre-Cambrian and the younger history of the earth. Now, as we have seen already in Chapter III, the only difference is that from that time onwards we find enough fossils to permit a relative dating of the younger rocks. In contrast, the pre-Cambrian has only been devided, very loosely, into Archaeic and Algonkian, or into Azoic and Proteozoic. These divisions are, however, practically meaningless for lack of fossils. Correlations of pre-Cambrian rocks found on different continents are without any factual foundation.

Only now, with the use of absolute dating techniques, has the unravelling of the structure and the history of the old shields become a possibility. The reader should be very wary, consequently, of any older conclusions about age relationships of rocks from any of the old shields. Moreover, as may be said of other fields too, such conclusions are often the more sweeping, the fewer the facts they are based on.

The apparent difference between the old shields and the younger areas of the crust is not that the old shields are so different in structure, but that we know next to nothing about them. That the old shields are indicated simply by stippling does not mean an absence of structures in these shields, but that we do not know how to correlate local structures into an overall picture.

So let us just point out here the location of the old shields, as given in Fig. 15. In a certain sense, the old shields form the cores of the continents. There are a Canadian, a Fennoscandian and a complex Asian shields on the northern hemisphere. On the southern hemisphere we find corresponding shields in Brazil, South Africa and Australia. There are smaller detached areas, such as Madagascar and India. Anyone familiar with geology knows that it is just those areas which have formed the subject of much theorizing about their former position.

STABILITY OF OLD SHIELDS

This again we may leave to the specialists, and come back to our statement that only within these old shields can vestiges of the origin of life on earth, and of the early life itself, be found. Everywhere else younger rocks have covered the pre-Cambrian basement. In these younger areas we now may distinguish regions where the crust remained relatively stable, and the pre-Cambrian basement was covered only by a not too thick pile of sediments. These regions, which more or less surround the old shields, are left blank in Fig. 15. Elsewhere the crust has subsided much more strongly. This resulted in the formation of definite geosynclinal basins, which became filled with very thick piles of sediments, and subsequently developed into the fold belts of orogenetic cycles. Three of the most important of these orogenetic cycles since the beginning of the Cambrian have been indicated in Fig. 15.

From this presentation it follows that the old shields, and also large areas around them, remained more or less stable during later history. New orogenetic cycles often develop outside the former ones, leaving the older terrain undisturbed. The older areas are, in some mysterious way, solidified. A rather naive comparison is often made between the sediments folded during an earlier orogenetic cycle, and corrugated iron which also is stronger than sheet iron. Although this comparison in all probability is unwarranted, it may well help to visualize this distinction between areas of the crust apparently solidified by earlier orogenies, and those which later became mobilized and developed into geosynclinal basins in younger orogenetic cycles.

This distinction is important in our search for areas where vestiges of early life may be found. On the stable platforms of older orogenetic cycles, newer sediments may be deposited from time to time in later history. But, these newer sediments remain thin when compared to the thick piles of sediment deposited in geosynclinal basins. Such a thin cover of younger sediments does not lead to such high pressures, nor to a very much higher temperature in the underlying rocks. When these rocks of the basement are again uplifted in a later period and the covering of younger sediments is eroded away, the basement rocks will not show too high a metamorphism, not too strong a recrystallization of their constituent minerals. So it is only in the anciently stabilized parts of the crust that we may hope to find undisturbed fossil remains of early life.

An example of this difference in metamorphism between rocks of similar age according to whether they have been laid down in a geosynclinal basin of an orogenetic cycle or on a stable platform, can be found in the European Cambrian. All around the old shield of Fennoscandia, the core of the European continent, sediments were laid down from the Cambrian to the Silurian. In Norway and Scotland a geosynclinal basin formed, which in turn developed into the Caledonian orogeny, with very thick series of sediments. Farther east much thinner series were deposited on the stable pre-Cambrian basement. The rocks in the Caledonian foldbelt are all more or less strongly metamorphosed, whilst those on the stable platform were affected so little that around Moscow bricks are made of soft clays of Cambrian age.

COMPLEX STRUCTURE OF OLD SHIELDS

In contrast to the impression evoked by the uniform stippling by which the old shields are indicated in many geology textbooks, they are built similarly to the younger regions of the crust. In the shields too, a succession of older and younger orogenetic belts can be found, whilst part of the areas of preceding orogenetic cycles have no longer been mobilized by subsequent orogenies. The old shields consequently are not a simple and uniform area forming the core of later structures. They themselves consist of older and still older cores, surrounded, and sometimes also cut up, by newer orogenetic belts. This is indicated in Fig. 15 where a number of absolute dates is given for various points of these shields. It is seen at a glance that the ages of various parts of the shields, often in quite close proximity, can show very great variations. A certain number of the major pre-Cambrian orogenies is indicated in Table III.

Of course, the further back we go into the history of the earth, the smaller are these oldest cores, which were already stabilized by an even older orogenetic cycle, and the greater the chance that during some subsequent orogeny the crust became mobilized, with the resulting geosynclines destroying all earlier fossils through metamorphism and recrystallization. So, the older the rock, the greater the chance that some unfortunate mishap has destroyed any fossils which it might possibly have carried. This, in combination with the fact that all early life was of a microbic nature, will explain the meagre fossil finds of early life on earth. The abundant fossils from the Cambrian onward are 'only' $1/2$ billion years old at most. Research into early life and its origin brings us back to the 1 billion and 2 billion, and even to the 3 billion-year age bracket.

CHAPTER VII

THE FOSSILS

It has been stated already that the fossil record of early life on earth is deplorably scanty. This statement is, perhaps, in need of qualification, for there is a rather extensive literature on fossils from the pre-Cambrian. But by and large these all come from sediments of late pre-Cambrian times. So they are not so much older, and clearly the precursors of the more fully developed and better preserved Cambrian faunae.

This late pre-Cambrian life comprises fossil remnants, including Algae, Radiolaria and Crustaceans, indicating the existence of a rich and varied flora and fauna, which was no longer restricted to microbes. These late pre-Cambrian organisms already belonged to higher levels of organization than those we must look for when we study early life on earth and its origin. Crustaceans, segmented animals with a hard outer skeleton, are as far removed from the origin of life as a jet aircraft is from a wheelbarrow.

Consequently these fossil assemblages of late pre-Cambrian times, which are known from several of the old shields, add but little to the knowledge of early life. They are all from sediments laid down only a little earlier than the base of the Cambrian system. They form the immediate ancestry of the organic world of the Cambrian. Their absolute age will not have been much higher than the 600 my which is now given for the base of the Cambrian; it will, in all probability, be much lower than 1 billion years.

THE IMPORTANCE OF MICROBES

This matter of the late pre-Cambrian organisms, which are the immediate precursors of those of the Cambrian, and which already show a high level of organization, brings up the importance of mi-

crobes, not only in early life, but also in our present environment.
This is in clear contrast to the somewhat supercilious way microbes
are treated by paleontology. Of course, this attitude, the way in
which most paleontology textbooks appear to forget the very existence of microbes, now or in the geological past, stems from the
extreme scarcity of fossilized microbe remains. Only under extremely
rare circumstances of fossilization, say, silicification or burial in
swamps, is there the slightest possibility that microbe remains can be
preserved over the lengths of geological time.

This is an unhappy circumstance, because of the importance microbes have not only in themselves, but for all other life. In our
present world they make up three quarters of living matter by sheer
weight, whilst they are unsurpassed in the variety of their metabolic
processes. Not only that, but many life processes of microbes form
the basis of daily functions of the higher organisms. Even if life of
the higher organisms is possible without microbes, as seems indicated
by experiments under carefully sterilized conditions, and if this were
possible in nature also, we might ask with Kluyver: "Is this life as
we know it? Is life without microbes really life? Is it worth living;
without bread and wine or cheese and beer?"

Of course, the importance of microbes for early life is even greater,
because they also are the evolutionary basis for all later forms with
higher organization. It follows that, in our search for the remnants
of early life, we must turn away from normal paleontology, which is
mainly interested in well-preserved hard parts of higher organisms,
which can be nicely classified and interpreted into evolutionary
schemata. We must look for remains of early microbes and other
forms of life with a low organization, and deduce from their extremely scarce remains the development and history of early life on
earth. The scarcity of these remains obliges us to tell our story in
but a very general way.

EARLY PRE-CAMBRIAN REMAINS

If we go back really further than those late pre-Cambrian organisms,
we only have a small number of finds. The earliest, which still are
the oldest in absolute age too, are those of lime-secreting organisms,
often loosely termed Algae, of South Africa, described by MacGregor.
Although quite convincing, this is not a case of real fossils, of struc-

turally preserved remnants of early organisms. Instead, it is a secretion of lime by early organisms, comparable to the crusts of travertine limestone, secreted at present by Algae during their metabolism. But even as such, it remains up till now the oldest indication of the existence of life on earth.

A more recent discovery, on the contrary, is of real fossils. These are the silicified primitive plants described by Tyler and Barghoorn from the old shield of Canada, which have been structurally preserved in microscopic detail. Their absolute age is, however, very much smaller than that of the organic deposits found by MacGregor in South Africa.

From Central Africa too, there are many other finds of limestone deposits formed by early organisms. This group shows a great resemblance, and is probably related to a type which extends into much younger time. This is *Collenia,* known from several old shields, which forms large colonies, and even bioherms (reefs) from late pre-Cambrian to Silurian times. Reference will here be made to the description of Gravelle and Lelubre, but there are many other finds of similar remains. In this case, although again we have no real fossils but deposits of lime secreted by early organisms, the structure and large size of individual colonies, together with their rather common occurrence, indicate a prolific life at the time of their formation. The absolute dating of these remains still rests, however, on the vaguest of indications and before we know if these forms are really that very old, much more reliable dates will have to be supplied.

THE OLDEST BIOGENIC DEPOSITS

The setting of the oldest remains formed by organic activity known up to now is South Africa, and more particularly Southern Rhodesia in the Bulawayo area. The pre-Cambrian series there are mainly formed by crystalline schists and metamorphosed ultrabasic rocks, by granitic batholites and dikes and by old volcanics — all rocks in which no vestiges of early life will ever be found. But there are also remains of relatively unmetamorphosed sediments, also laid down in pre-Cambrian times. Of these the Dolomite series, which is quarried for lime in the Bulawayo area, is of particular interest. The areas where these old sediments are still preserved are separated by metamorphic and igneous rocks, so it is difficult to establish a detailed

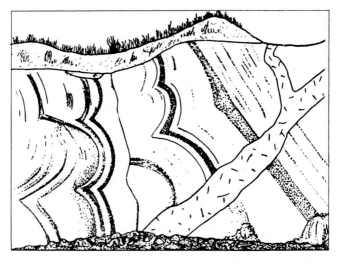

Fig. 16. West face of a limestone quarry near Bulawayo, Southern Rhodesia. Length about 5 m. Pre-Cambrian dolomite series with biogenic structures, cut by younger granitic dike (from MacGregor, 1940).

stratigraphy of the Dolomite series. It is, however, certain that it has a very great age, for it is cut by younger granitic veins, and absolute dating of these veins gives 2,670 my, or roughly 2.7 billion years. Consequently, the rocks of the Dolomite series are certainly older than 2.7 billion years.

The Dolomite series consists of limestone and dolomite (limestone containing magnesium). In the limestone peculiarly layered structures occur in definite beds. They show series of domes, or of finer dentate forms, on their upper surface, whilst under closer inspection they are seen to be built up by sequences of fine layers which more or less follow the outer surface. These layers, which may be as much as 3 mm apart in the central part of the domes, do narrow considerably outwards. Better than by words, these structures can be represented by the pictures taken from the quarry wall, which indicate their general form, and from polished or etched surfaces, giving their detailed structure (Figs. 16-19). Important to note is the dome-like or dentate form; the fact that they occur in definite beds; and their finely layered microstructure. The latter shows a certain degree of regularity, which we know so well from lime deposits of later Algae, or from early Coelenterata, but which is, on the other hand, too irregular for any inorganic rhythmic deposit. MacGregor (1940) justly concludes that these are biogenic deposits, formed by lime-secreting organisms at the time the beds of the Dolomite series were formed.

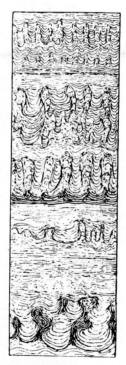

Fig. 17. Series of probably biogenic pre-Cambrian limestone deposits in parallel beds. Dolomite series, near Bulawayo, Southern Rhodesia (x $^1/_{40}$) (from Young, 1940 a).

Fig. 18.

Fig. 19. Thin section of biogenic pre-Cambrian limestone deposit, dolomite series, near Bulawayo, Southern Rhodesia (slightly reduced)
(from MacGregor, 1940).

Fig. 18. Polished and etched surface of biogenic deposits in pre-
Cambrian limestone. Dolomite series, near Bulawayo, Southern Rhodesia (x $^3/_4$). Fine lamellar structure in so-called 'dentate band' in-
dicates biogenic deposition rather than inorganic recrystallization of
limestone (from MacGregor, 1940). Scale shows inches.

Because of the similarity with deposits of lime-secreting Algae found in later geologic history and at present, the Rhodesian deposits are commonly called 'algal limestones'. This similarity has even led some scientists to look for later algal lime deposits of exactly similar build, and on that feature alone to conclude to a definite taxonomic relationship of the organisms which formed these deposits.

ANOXYGENIC METABOLISM OF EARLIEST KNOWN ORGANISMS

Although it is by way of this close similarity in structure between the Rhodesian deposits and later algal deposits that we are justified to conclude that the Rhodesian deposits, too, are formed by organisms, that they really are biogenic, any further conclusions on taxonomic relationship to later forms, or even a designation as 'Algae' is unwarranted.

2.7 Billion years ago, there must still have existed the pre-actualistic atmosphere. MacGregor's lime-secreting organisms were therefore anoxygenic, and consequently far removed in systematic position from all later oxygenic Algae of the actualistic atmosphere. We can but guess at the peculiar anoxygenic metabolism which already led to lime secretion by these early organisms, but they cannot have been related at all to any of the systematic groups in which the present oxygenic life and its fossil parentage are cut up in taxonomic procedure. Biochemically, it seems that lime secretion in anoxygenic metabolism presents no difficulties. There are even various anoxygenic metabolistic schemes possible which would yield energy to the organism and at the same time secrete lime (Kluyver, in lit.).

STRUCTURES IN BIOGENIC AND INORGANIC LIMESTONE DEPOSITS

It is well, at this point, I think, to clarify why we are so emphatic that the remains described by MacGregor are biogenic; that they really are deposits formed by organisms. They are not real fossils, because they are not the structurally-preserved remains of the organisms themselves. Just as with the later lime-secreting Algae, we may even presume that these early organisms did not have a definite morphological structure, but instead formed more or less irregular masses. It is the finely lamellar structure of these deposits which is so typically biogenic. This not only closely resembles the structure of lime deposits formed by later Algae and other organisms, but it is, moreover, quite distinct from any structure which may develop in limestone through inorganic processes.

Intricate structures in limestone may also be formed inorganically, either closely following upon sedimentation or in a later geologic period, through solution, pressure, or other factors, without any intervention of organisms. But such structures, of which the well-known 'cone-in-cone' is the most distinctive, never even distantly resemble biogenic limestone deposits with their peculiar wavy, regular — irregular microlamination. In the Dolomite series of Southern Rhodesia such inorganic structures do also occur. Consequently Young, who gave an over-all appraisal of the 'algal' structures of the Dolomite series (Young, 1940 a), describes in a companion paper (Young, 1940 b) other structures of the Dolomite series which are absolutely at variance with the 'algal' structures, and which are thought to have nothing to do with early life. Not every abnormal structure consequently is thought to be biogenic, and the structures described by MacGregor underwent a most thorough appraisal before they were offered and accepted as proof of the existence of life datable as at least 2.7 billion years old.

THE OLDEST REAL FOSSILS

The fossils of primitive plants described by Tyler and Barghoorn (1954) are found in the Gunflint iron formation of the pre-Cambrian of the Canadian Old Shield, in southern Ontario. They are described to occur in cherts, an American synonym for the British flint, within a series containing iron ores. Flints or cherts, are deposits of microcrystalline quartz, SiO_2. The Gunflint chert has evidently been used for the flintlocks of early guns in colonial times.

Such siliceous sediments are often formed in a swampy environment, where humic acid deriving from the swamp vegetation acidifies the groundwater so that it attacks calcareous or phosphate organic animal remains such as bones or shells. But cellulose and other plant substances are relatively resistant to these acid waters, and plant remains can consequently be fossilized in such an environment through a replacement, molecule by molecule, of their original substances by silica. Mineral stains derived from the original organic material may colour these silicified fossils, so that the original structure may sometimes still be observed in the minutest detail. Silicifica-

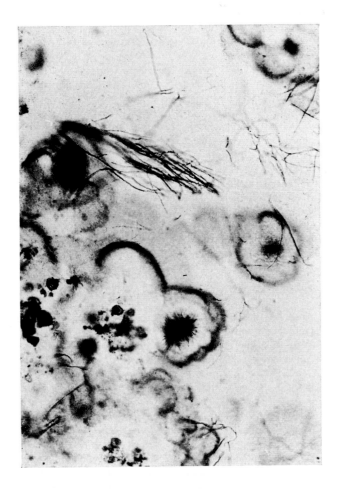

Fig. 20. Microphotograph of silicified fossils of primitive algal plants from the Gunflint formation of Ontario, 1600 my old (x 325). Two different types are seen, one forming globose colonies, the other forming free, unbranched filaments (from Tyler and Barghoorn, 1954).

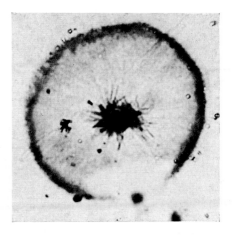

Fig. 21. Microphotograph of single globose colony of primitive algal plants. Detail of Fig. 20 x 725 (from Tyler and Barghoorn, 1954).

tion consequently provides us with the most beautifully preserved plant remains. 'Silicified woods', for instance, are known from many localities and various geologic formations, and are often preserved in natural parks.

Due to this silicification, the early plant life of the Gunflint iron formation has been preserved in an amazing wealth of detail, as can be seen from the photographs of thin sections with extreme magnification, taken by Professors Tyler and Barghoorn and reproduced here by their kind permission (Figs. 20-23).

PRIMITIVE PLANTS FROM ONTARIO

A preliminary note by Tyler and Barghoorn (1954) so far contains all published data. Much more work has been done, which will be fully reviewed in a forthcoming description (Barghoorn, 1962). Anyone interested in these earliest fossils will have to consult this work for full information, because here only a general review can be given.

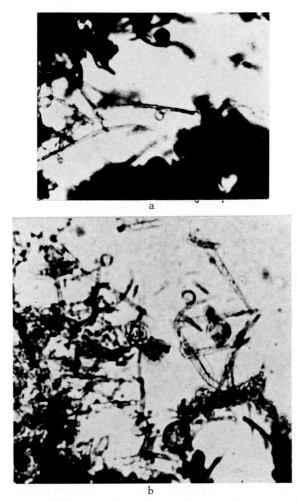

a

b

Fig. 22. Microphotographs of silicified fossils of primitive fungal plants from the Gunflint formation of Ontario, 1600 my old. Shown are portions of mycelium and detached (a) and sessile (b) spores (a x 725, b x 750) (from Tyler and Barghoorn, 1954).

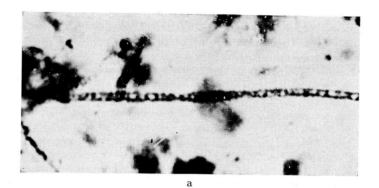

a

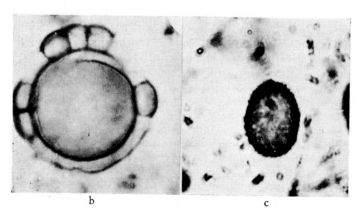

b   c

Fig. 23. Microphotographs of silicified fossils of primitive plants from
the Gunflint formation of Ontario, 1600 my old, strongly magnified, to
show minute detail conserved by silicification. Unpublished photographs,
courtesy professors Elso S. Barghoorn and S. A. Tyler (a x 1600,
b x 1500, c x 1800).

The important points of the Gunflint fossils are, first, that they are real fossils, being structurally-preserved remains of organisms; secondly, that remains are found of several quite different plants, indicating the existence already at that time of a diversified, although of course primitive, flora; and lastly, their great age, which is now thought to be 1600 my.

Thus far, to quote the 1954 paper of Tyler and Barghoorn, five distinct organic forms have been recognized, four multicellular, and one unicellular. Two of the former are related to algae and two others to fungi. Their form is best seen from the accompanying photographs (Figs. 20-23). Microbiologists who have studied the original thin sections agree without the slightest hesitation that all these are really fossilized remains of simple plants and microbes. The amazing fact, to my mind, is that this is not only proof of the existence of life at that time, but also of the high level of diversification it had already attained. We are already far removed from the beginning, when all life was still represented by microbes, because there is already a definite variety of simple forms of higher plant life.

The age of these earliest fossils was not easily settled at first. In 1954 only helium measurements were available, not even from the Gunflint formation itself in Ontario, but from magnetite of the Negaunee iron formation in Michigan, which was correlated in a rather loose way with the Gunflint, and thought to have a slightly younger or about the same age. The helium datings, notoriously untrustworthy, ranged from 800 my to 1650 my, averaging 1300 my. The plant fossils were found near the base of the Gunflint, however, and consequently an age approaching 2 billion years was thought likely. It is this figure which has since been repeated in the literature, trying to make the 'oldest fossils' as old as possible. Later, as yet unpublished rubidium—strontium determinations of the Gunflint iron formation itself gave consistent absolute ages of 1600 my (Barghoorn, in lit.), the figure which is provisionally accepted here.

Apart from the absolute age of these earliest fossils, the question of their environment is of importance. Did these primitive plants still live under a pre-actualistic atmosphere, or did they already belong to actual life, living under a normal oxygenic atmosphere? At the present state of our knowledge this cannot be decided. As will be discussed in the next chapter, the Blind River uraniferous deposits, roughly 2 billion years old, and situated in the same general area, were still formed under anoxygenic conditions. This difference in absolute age of some 400 my corroborates earlier geologic correlations, which also seem to indicate that the Gunflint is much younger than Blind River. So it is quite possible that the earliest fossils from the Gunflint did already live under the oxygenic atmosphere. The fact that in this formation cherts and iron ore seem to be separated also points in the same direction, according to the studies of Lepp and Goldich reviewed in the next chapter. At present, the best we can do is to state as a considered guess that the earliest fossils known up to now, the primitive plants described by Tyler and Barghoorn, lived already under the actualistic, oxygenic atmosphere.

REEFS OF ALGAL LIMESTONE IN THE SAHARA

The biogenic deposits described from the pre-Cambrian of Central Africa, amongst others by Gravelle and Lelubre, form a welcome

Fig. 24. Reef of *Conophyton* in the Pharusian. Pre-Cambrian of the Hoggar, Sahara (from Gravelle and Lelubre, 1954, Plate XXVII).

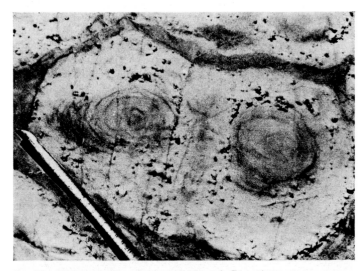

Fig. 25. Detailed view of two colonies of *Conophyton* in transverse section. Pharusian, pre-Cambrian of the Hoggar, Sahara (from Gravelle and Lelubre, 1954, Plate XXVIII).

addition to those described from South Africa by MacGregor. They are found mainly in the central Sahara, in the general district of the Hoggar. They too are no real fossils, but crusts of limestone deposited by lime-secreting organisms. Comparing these with the earliest deposits of limestone from South Africa, we find that there is ever so much more of them. Both in number of localities and in volume of the limestone deposited, they far exceed their South African counterpart. The age of the deposits from the Sahara is not well known, but it probably is much less than that of the MacGregor deposits.

The remains from the pre-Cambrian of the Sahara are classed as belonging to the Stromatolites, an artificial taxonomic group comprising masses of limestone, sometimes globose, sometimes more tubular, which do not have a clear microstructure, and which often occur in colonies of considerable size. The colonies may form reefs, or, more technically, bioherms. Such reefs are mounds or layers constructed by the organisms themselves, in contrast to normal sediments which have been laid down, either through setting by gravity, or through secretion by chemical processes. Algal reefs of the group of the Stromatolites are the earliest bioherms known in geologic history.

The best-known of these reef-building, lime-secreting organisms amongst the group of the Stromatolites is *Collenia,* which forms colonies of globose concretions of limestone, each up to several decimeters in diameter. In the Sahara not only *Collenia* is found, but also other remains, belonging to the form genus *Conophyton.* An example of a reef built by the latter organisms is reproduced in Figs. 24 and 25.

The main importance of *Collenia* lies, however, not in the fact that it is the textbook form of early algal limestone secretions and of early algal reefs, but in the fact that it is not restricted to the pre-Cambrian. It persists even into the Ordovician. It is consequently contemporaneous with early representatives of all the main groups of modern life.

The fact that *Collenia* persists into the Ordovician proves that it is a representative of modern, actualistic life. Its metabolism was oxygenic. In view of the similarity between the limestone secretions of *Collenia* and other Stromatolites, there is, consequently, no objection to class the group of Stromatolites with the Algae, and to speak of algal limestones.

The fact that Stromatolites belong to modern life is important for a general idea of their age. Because they belong to modern life, to the actualistic atmosphere, they are certainly much younger than their South African counterparts described by MacGregor, which still belong to the pre-actualistic atmosphere. How much younger they are, is, however, difficult to say. The fact is that, beyond the indication that they belong to the pre-Cambrian, we have no trustworthy dating at all to arrive at an estimate of the Sahara deposits. Geologically, they belong to the formation called Pharusian. This formation is distinctly younger than the strongly metamorphosed rocks which form the basement in the Sahara. On the other hand, the Pharusian is definitely older than late pre-Cambrian rocks, now often classed as Infra-Cambrian, because they belong to the same suite as the Cambrian. According to this position, the Pharusian is said to belong to the Middle pre-Cambrian. But it is clear that this is a very vague classification only, based exclusively on relative techniques of correlation and dating, which do not supply a basis for absolute dating.

We consequently cannot agree with Furon (1960), who gives an age of between 3 billion and 2 billion years for the Middle pre-Cambrian of the Sahara. This age is not based on a sufficient number of absolute datings. Even if some members of the series of very different rocks grouped together as Pharusian should really be that old, this age certainly does not apply to the recrystallized limestones with reefs of *Collenia* or *Conophyton*. These must be younger than 2 billion years, because they are representatives of modern, actualistic life.

To conclude, the pre-Cambrian biogenic deposits of *Collenia* and *Conophyton* in the Sahara are younger than 2 billion years, but we cannot even assess a minimum age, beyond the fact that they are older than late pre-Cambrian. Their probable age falls somewhere between 2 billion and 1 billion years. In view of the many localities in Central Africa where such remains of *Stromatolites* are found, it would be very important to have some more dependable figures for their absolute age.

OPTIMISTIC OUTLOOK

After having reviewed in some detail the three most important remains of early life on earth, I think it is appropriate to end this chapter on an optimistic note. Although geologic remains of early life are scanty indeed, they leave no doubt that there was life on earth in the dawn of geologic history. Moreover, we have seen that there was already life on earth under the early anoxygenic, pre-actualistic atmosphere. This lends weight to the speculative theories of biologists and astronomers according to which all present free oxygen is biogenic.

So, although the remains of early life found up to now are scanty, they are very revealing. Even these scanty finds have taught us a great deal about early life on earth. We have advanced very much in our knowledge during the last two decades.

The scarcity of remains of early life on earth is to be expected. Early life will have been largely microbic, for one thing, and thus was not of the easily fossilizing type. Also, rocks of such great age are generally either rendered almost unrecognizable through metamorphism, or buried by younger rocks. Geologic study of the old shields is, however, rapidly expanding. Hence, it is really not too optimistic to expect that much further information on this subject will turn up in the near future; nor is it too optimistic to hope for as large a stride forward to be taken during the coming decades, as has been taken during the last two.

Chapter VIII

THE ENVIRONMENT

WEATHERING OF ROCKS

Apart from the actual finds of fossilized remains, geology can also evaluate the conditions which reigned at a certain time on the surface of the earth. That is, in those cases where enough data are preserved upon which to base some concept, geology can make out whether there possibly has been, in the early past, a reducing atmosphere: an atmosphere totally different from our present oxidizing one, such as is postulated by biologists and astronomers.

As stated before, this is possible because such a different atmosphere would not only affect life, but also chemical processes on the surface of the earth. Such a reducing atmosphere would make its influence felt in all contemporary exogenic processes.

The most important of the exogenic processes for our problem, is the sequence weathering—erosion—transportation—sedimentation. Dependent upon local characteristics of erosion—transportation—sedimentation, such as speed of transportation, sedimentation on lowlands or in oceans, weathering may take place during the latter parts of this sequence too. For a determination of the character of the early atmosphere the type of weathering in those days is of paramount importance. The influence of the other exogenic processes serves more or less as a background for its setting.

To look further into the effects of weathering, it is necessary first to make a short digression, and review the composition of the rocks of the earth's crust, because this now enters into the picture. The most common elements of the crust are silica, Si, aluminium, Al and oxygen, O. Most minerals of the crust are compounds of these elements, either silicium oxide or quartz, SiO_2, or silicates: compounds of Si, O and Al. Into the silicate compounds are incorporated the base metals Ca and Mg, the alkalis K and Na, metals, such as

Fe, and, of course, anions, H and the halogens; S and so on.

Silicates containing only alkalis and Ca combined with aluminium and silica, mostly form light-coloured felspars. Dark minerals, like biotite, augite and hornblende, also contain Mg, Fe and other metals. The three groups of quartz, felspars and dark minerals together make up by far the bulk of all crustal rocks. In addition ore minerals occur, mainly in plutonic rocks and related veins. These contain sulphides, like pyrites, FeS, and metal oxides like magnetite, Fe_3O_4. The sulphides in general are low-temperature minerals, the oxides are formed at much higher temperature.

Returning now to the process of weathering of rocks exposed at the surface of the earth, we find that weathering attacks the crustal rocks along two main lines: physical and chemical. Pure physical weathering is rare. It is found, for instance, both in extremely cold and in extremely hot and dry climates; in the tundras and the deserts. In a cold climate rocks disintregate through frost splitting, in the desert through sun blasting. Everywhere else on earth chemical weathering is present, whilst it normally forms the main line of attack on rocks of the crust.

MINERALS UNSTABLE IN PRESENT WEATHERING

Chemical weathering, under the circumstances of our present oxidizing atmosphere, will attack all minerals but the oxides. Both the felspars and the common dark minerals of the normal rocks, as well as the sulphides of the ore veins, will be oxidized and form soluble compounds. So the only things left are the oxides: the common quartz, and the much rarer ore oxides such as magnetite. The solutions carrying the material from the felspars, the dark minerals and the ore sulphides are transported by rivers into lowlands and oceans. There, mostly below the watertable, and often at the exclusion of free oxygen, new compounds will form. The new combinations predominantly belong to the group of the clay minerals.

This is, in an extremely schematized version, the normal sequence of weathering—transportation—sedimentation in our present oxidative atmosphere. Although extremely simplified, it illustrates the points important for our study: that all minerals except oxides are unstable in regard to chemical weathering, and, moreover, that the ions derived from that chemical weathering of silicates and sulphides,

upon being transported into areas of sedimentation, may recombine
to form clay minerals.

That is the reason why we now have only three types of sediment:
sand, clay and limestone. The sands are exclusively quartz sands, the
left-overs of chemical weathering, although perhaps transported and
re-sedimented several times. The clays are newly formed by re-
combination of ions derived through chemical weathering from silicates. The carbonate material of the limestones is mainly of a biogenic origin, derived from animal shells.

Only under exceptional circumstances will, for instance, sand still
contain an appreciable amount of felspar. This occurs when detritus
of igneous rocks is deposited quite near to its source area, and
speedily buried in such a way that further chemical weathering is
prevented. Sulphides, which do not only weather more quickly, but
are also readily attacked through biochemical action by sulphur
bacteria, nowadays are found even more rarely in sands. There are
some examples from high up in the tundras, where the fiercely cold
climate is prohibitive of chemical erosion, or from the rapidly sub-
siding Indus valley, where younger sediments, quickly covering older
deposits, effectively seal off the air supply and thereby prevent further
weathering. These exceptions, by their scarcity, and by the ex-
tremeness of the conditions of their environment, only stress the
more strongly that normally in our present oxidative atmosphere all
sands are quartz sands; the only stable minerals are oxides.

MINERALS STABLE UNDER ANOXYGENIC ATMOSPHERE

This will not have been so under a primeval atmosphere of reducing
character. There, felspars, dark minerals and sulphides could have
lain on the surface of the earth for a much longer time before they
finally disintregrated. They even could have been taken up in a new
erosion—transportation—sedimentation sequence; for instance, when
through slight crustal movements, through a changing of river courses,
or lowering of the sea level, their original sedimentation area would
become attacked by erosion. They would weather much more through
mechanical attack, and much less through chemical weathering. Consequently in repeated sequences of erosion—transportation—sedimentation, they would become well rounded and get well sorted as to
size and specific weight.

Under such a reducing atmosphere one would expect that sands of all sorts of composition would be formed — coarser and finer sands of the lighter minerals, such as quartz plus felspar (not quartz alone), or sands of medium-weight minerals such as hornblende and augite. But also sands of the heavy ore minerals like sulphides and metal-oxides. The size, form and specific weight of the individual grains, their physical properties, would determine their ultimate place of sedimentation, not their chemical properties.

STUDIES BY RANKAMA: DETRITUS OF GRANITES

A first attempt to use the difference in exogenic processes under anoxygenic or oxygenic atmospheres, was made by Rankama (1955) in Finland. He tried to evaluate the character of the atmosphere by studying an ancient deposit of detrital rocks around a granitic rock from which the sediments were thought to be derived. The granitic body, actually a quartz diorite, contains about four per cent ferrous iron and two per cent of ferric iron, measured by weight of the oxides. Now in oxidative weathering, the relative amount of ferric iron will normally always be greater in sediments derived from a granite, because of oxidation of the ferrous iron. In the Finland example, this is not the case, the ratio Fe_2O_3/FeO in the sediments is even lower than that of an original diorite pebble included in the sediments, and it is comparable to that of neighbouring quartz diorites (Table V).

Rankama concluded that this particular quartz diorite weathered under reducing atmospheric circumstances. This gives us a fixed date for the existence of the early anoxygenic atmosphere if the age of the sediments could be established.

The pre-Cambrian stratigraphy of the Fennoskandian old shield, however, is very much under study at the moment, and absolute dating tends to reverse many of the earlier correlations. The quartz diorite and the derived sediments studied by Rankama were formerly grouped with the Botnian period. This was thought to be somewhat earlier than the Svecofennian period, which was dated at around 1800 my. Nowadays, Botnian and Svecofennian are sometimes lumped together, and the 1800 my age is then thought to be that of a younger metamorphosis, and not to give the real age of the rocks. More facts will undoubtedly become available in the near future.

TABLE V

FERROUS AND FERRIC IRON CONTENT (WEIGHT PER CENT) IN QUARTZ
DIORITES AND DERIVED SEDIMENTS OF MIDDLE PRE-CAMBRIAN
AGE NEAR TAMPERE, FINLAND
(from Rankama, 1955)

	Quartz diorite pebble	Quartz diorites					
Fe_2O_3	1.98	0.79	0.61	0.75	1.46	0.50	1.09
FeO	3.67	6.70	4.06	6.23	7.99	4.35	5.65
Fe_2O_3/FeO	0.54	0.12	0.15	0.12	0.18	0.11	0.19
		Derived sediments					
Fe_2O_3		0.16	1.73	0.49	0.65	1.43	
FeO		2.94	5.19	5.06	6.31	6.71	
Fe_2O_3/FeO		0.05	0.33	0.10	0.10	0.21	

Until that time a tentative age of 2 billion years may be provisionally assigned to the reductive weathering processes described by Rankama in Finland.

Rankama's assertion that the ancient sediments are really derived from that particular granitic rock, the quartz diorites, whose relative abundance in ferrous and ferric iron tallies so well with that of the surrounding schists, is, however, open to question. There are many granites in the area, there is a regional metamorphism of the enclosing sediments, and it is rather difficult to establish beyond doubt the relation between granitic rock and metamorphosed sediments. Rankama's study has, however, shown the way in which ancient sediments can be used to assess the properties of the atmosphere of the earth at the time of their deposition. Rankama's ideas have later been amplified by quite independent studies by the German ore specialist Ramdohr. In the latter case the material is quite different, but the same basic assumption underlies the work of both Rankama and Ramdohr.

STUDIES BY RAMDOHR: GOLD—URANIUM REEFS

The study of Ramdohr (1958) describes ancient pre-Cambrian deposits from the old shields of South Africa, Brazil and Canada, which are of economic importance for their gold—uranium content. But quite apart from their economic importance, they have a more general significance in that they are formed by ancient sands and gravels. They represent sediments laid down on the surface of the earth in an exogenic process. Consequently their composition was influenced by that of the ancient contemporary atmosphere. These deposits are formed not only by grains of quartz, but also by sulphides and by pitchblende. Pitchblende now is a complex mineral with a composition somewhere between UO_2 and U_3O_8. This is due, however, to later oxidizing. Originally, it consisted of the mineral uraninite, UO_2, the least oxidized of the uranium oxides. The South African deposits are gold reefs, already mined for their gold, to which the uranium has added an appreciable factor. The Brazilian and Canadian deposits, although formed by quite similar reefs, are so low in gold that they only recently acquired economic importance as uranium ores. The deposits described by Ramdohr belong to the following districts: Witwatersrand and Dominion Reef, South Africa; Serra de Jacobina, Bahia, Brazil; and Blind River, Ontario, Canada. There is thus a wide variation in their geographical position, whilst there is also, as we will see, a very marked difference in age.

Notwithstanding this separation in geographical position, or the difference in age, their composition is strikingly similar. So similar that even the experts often cannot tell samples of one district from those of any of the other three. The mineral composition shows, of course, quite strong variations from bed to bed. Also lateral variations within a single horizon may occur in the relative abundance of the constituent minerals. But the over-all picture is remarkably consistent. The variations all fall within the same sharp limits. And — most important — this over-all picture, which is so strikingly similar for these ancient deposits, although they are so far removed in space and time, this over-all picture of these ancient deposits contrasts strongly with that of all younger gravel and sand of the later history of the earth.

SANDS WITH PYRITES, PITCHBLENDE AND OTHER MINERALS

The deposits are formed by ancient quartz conglomerates and quartz sands, cemented to a very hard rock which forms the reefs. But apart from the quartz they carry pyrites, FeS, ilmenite, $FeTiO_3$ and pitchblende, primarily UO_2, in considerable quantities.

They show all the characteristic features of deposits originally laid down as superficial gravels and sands. They form placer deposits. The roundness of the individual grains, the fact that they are so well sorted in grain size, the differences in mineral composition and in grain size between successive beds, are characteristics found in all gravels and sands superficially laid down from streams and lakes, and cannot be accounted for by any other process of deposition.

In these ancient deposits, which contain grains of such a different composition, and consequently of different specific weight, such as quartz, pyrite and pitchblende, it is nice to see how in one single horizon the lightest grains, the quartz grains, are always much larger than the heavier pyrite grains, whilst the much heavier grains of pitchblende are by far the smallest. This is one of the nicest examples of sorting and classifying of grains according to size and weight, according to physical properties, as one can find in geology.

Moreover, Ramdohr describes evidence of erosion of earlier beds of these ancient sands and gravels, and re-deposition of fragments of earlier clastic horizons in newer beds. One finds rolled lumps of the older deposits, re-deposited together with single grains in a younger bed.

There is a striking similarity in mode of deposition, of reworking and re-deposition of these ancient gravels and sands, with their contemporary erosion channels of ancient rivers, to much younger gravels and sands and to recent examples. There is but one difference, and that a paramount one; namely, all newer gravels and sands are formed by quartz only, whilst in these ancient deposits we find a large amount of grains of sulphides, of pitchblende and of other minerals, together with grains of quartz. These other minerals are not stable under the present oxygenic atmosphere.

The structure of these reefs can be studied in Figs. 26-32. Figs. 26 and 27 are respectively from an ancient sand of Witwatersrand, 1800 my old, and from a recent black sand from the coast north of Buenos Aires. The ancient sand consists mainly of pyrites, FeS, the recent sand of magnetite, Fe_3O_4, which have comparable specific weights. The similarity in structure is self-evident. But the pyrite sand would be unstable now, whereas the magnetite sand, formed by iron oxide, is stable under the present oxygenic atmosphere.

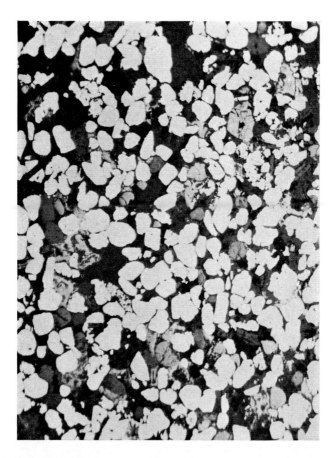

Fig. 26. Microphotograph of ancient sand, 1800 my old, from Witwatersrand, South Africa (x 70). White : grains of pyrite. Grey : grains of various oxides. Dark : grains of quartz (from Ramdohr, 1958).

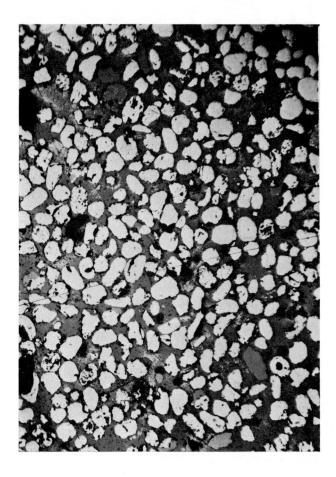

Fig. 27. Microphotograph of recent sand from the coast of the Argentine (x 45). White grains of magnetite. Compare with structure of
ancient pyrite sand of Fig. 26 (from Ramdohr, 1958).

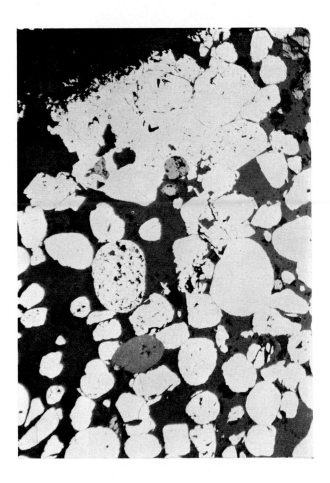

Fig. 28. Microphotograph of ancient pyrite—quartz sand, Witwatersrand, South Africa (x 45). White : grains of pyrite. Dark : grains of
quartz. At the top, lump of re-deposited older pyrite conglomerate.
Rounded borders of original pyrite grains within the older conglomerate
are still visible (from Ramdohr, 1958).

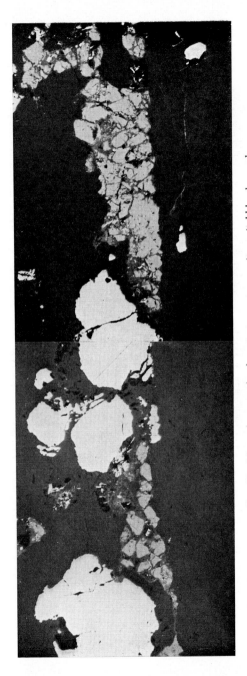

Fig. 29. Microphotograph of ancient quartz—pyrite—pitchblende sand, showing sedimentary rhythm. Blind River, Canada (x 22½). Black: quartz, individual grains not recognizable in reproduction. White: quartz, individual grains not recognizable in reproduction. White: pyrite. Dark grey: small grains of pitchblende (from Ramdohr, 1958).

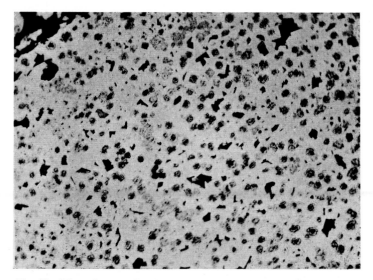

Fig. 30. Microphotograph of polished surface of grain of pyrite in ancient sand at Witwatersrand, South Africa (x 250). Dark spots indicate centres of biogenic deposition of iron sulphides by ancient microbes or fungi (from Ramdohr, 1958). In the original section, professor Ramdohr writes, these dark spots show a microstructure, not visible in reproduction. They are seen to be formed by a central dark point, surrounded by one or two small circles, which are in turn surrounded by the more or less rectangular spots that are clearly visible in this illustration. The central point and the surrounding circles are thought to represent the original 'pyrite bacteria', more probably fungi, which served as nuclei for further inorganic growth of pyrite crystals (Ramdohr). The age of these biogenic deposits is not known exactly, because they were found in polished surfaces of pebbles within the Witwatersrand deposits. Taking their age at 1800 my gives us a minimum age, but their original formation might have taken place much earlier. Finding of such small scale remnants, with high magnification ore microscopy, is greatly dependent on luck, and a systematic search for such structures in earlier deposits has not yet been carried out.

Fig. 28 is again from an ancient sand of Witwatersrand, which is formed mainly by quartz and pyrite. In this picture too, we see that the amount of sulphide grains is large compared to that of the quartz grains. The pyrite grains are not a negligible minority, as is the case with the 'heavy minerals' in recent sands. They form one of the main constituents. Moreover, at the upper side a re-deposited lump of an older conglomerate is found. The rounded borders of the older grains, cemented together in the lump of the earlier conglomerate, are still faintly seen.

Fig. 29 shows a sedimentary rhythm, in all aspects comparable to rhythms in sedimentation found in younger sands and gravels. On top of a bed of quartz grains lies a thin horizon composed of grains of pyrite and of pitchblende. The boundaries between the individual quartz grains are no longer seen in the reproduction. These grains are, however, much larger than those of the pyrite, whilst the pitchblende grains are not only the smallest, but moreover show a strict classification of size.

Indications were also found of the presence of life during the formation of these deposits. Fig. 30 shows a polished section of a pyrite grain at a higher magnification. The many spots seen are thought to represent centres of deposition of the iron sulphide, through the influence of early microbes.

The conclusion to be drawn from these deposits is that they were formed under a reducing, anoxygenic atmosphere.

Not every geologist will agree with this conclusion. This is caused by the fact that these reefs are very old, and consequently the primary structures of their sedimentation have often been obscured by later secondary processes. Pyrite and the other sulphides, and also gold, are easily mobilized and later re-deposited on secondary location, within the long times of later geologic history. Moreover, there is a constant bombardment through the radioactive decay of the uranium in the pitchblende grains which also tends to obliterate primary structures. If we look at the pyrite grains, for instance, we see how many rounded grains were later covered by new growths of pyrite now deposited along crystallographic planes, which tends to render the original roundness of the pyrite sand grains unrecognizable (Figs. 31 and 32). Some geologists have been led astray by these secondary phenomena, which they think to be of primary character.

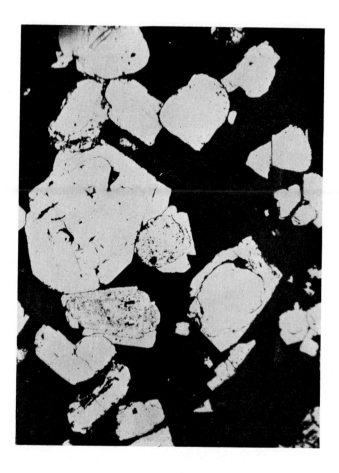

Fig. 31. Microphotograph of grains of pyrite in quartz in ancient sands of Witwatersrand, South Africa (x 70). The rounded grains show later growths of pyrite, formed after the deposition of the sands, which follow crystal planes, and tend to obliterate the roundness of the original pyrite sand grains (from Ramdohr, 1958).

Fig. 32. Microphotograph of rounded pyrite grain, surrounded by a younger deposit which has grown around the older grain, showing crystal form of pyrite (x 250). Serra de Jacobina, Brazil (from Ramdohr, 1958).

But the many properties of these deposits which fit the picture of ancient placer deposits, of ancient gravels and sands, together with the striking similarity between these deposits so widely separated geographically and in time, demonstrate that Ramdohr's interpretation is the correct one. A later study by Liebenberg (1960) moreover confirms these results.

Once this explanation is accepted, however, the omnipresence of grains of sulphides and of pitchblende in sands and gravels is convincing proof that their deposition took place under an atmosphere of reducive character in all of the four districts mentioned.

AGE OF SEDIMENTS FORMED UNDER ANOXYGENIC ATMOSPHERE

The tentative age of these deposits is given in Table VI.

Taking into account the tendency of tentative ages in absolute dating to grow older when better determinations become available, we may safely state that these deposits range from 2 billion to 3 billion years. This means that a reducing, anoxygenic atmosphere on earth was still present 2 billion years ago.

TABLE VI

TENTATIVE AGE OF THE GOLD—URANIUM DEPOSITS FORMED UNDER AN
ANOXYGENIC ATMOSPHERE AS STUDIED BY
RAMDOHR (1958)

Dominion Reef, South Africa	3000 my
Serra de Jacobina, Bahia, Brazil	?
Witwatersrand, South Africa	1800 my
Blind River, Ontario, Canada	1100 my *

STUDIES BY LEPP AND GOLDICH: IRON FORMATIONS

Lepp and Goldich (1959) reached conclusions quite similar to those arrived at by Ramdohr from the study of iron formations. Iron formations are superficially formed deposits of iron ore, such as the economically important iron ores in the old shield of North America found, for instance, around Lake Superior, or the minette ores of Jurassic age in Lotharingen and Luxembourg. Iron ore can also be found in veins, and most of the economically important iron deposits of early history and medieval times were formed by veins of iron ore.

* A figure of more than 1700 my (Derry, 1959) gives a more probable age.

An example which still has some economical value today, is found in the Siegerland in West Germany. In veins of iron ore the iron is deposited from solutions originating in deeper levels of the crust. Formation of veins of iron ore is an endogenic process, in contrast to that of the iron formations, which are formed by exogenic processes.

The latter are called lateritization, but this term covers a wide variety of different chemical reactions. Lateritization leads to a relative enrichment in iron of a parent rock, mainly through solution of its other components. The iron formations thus are residual ores, or, to put it in an oversimplified form, they are the left-overs from parent rocks through the influence of lateritization processes.

According to Lepp and Goldich, there is a marked and consistent distinction between the iron formations of the pre-Cambrian and younger ones. Those of the pre-Cambrian are siliceous, whilst in the later deposits iron and silica were separated by the lateritization processes operating during the later history of the earth. If we find younger siliceous iron formations, such as occur intercalated in the minette ores, these are clearly formed by a secondary silicification process which was later than the original lateritization. Lepp and Goldich now postulate that this difference between pre-Cambrian iron formations and all later deposits is due to a relative deficiency in oxygen of the pre-Cambrian atmosphere. This is an extremely cautious way of saying that the pre-Cambrian atmosphere was anoxygenic.

So the conclusion of Lepp and Goldich is in good agreement with the results of studies by Rankama and Ramdohr. It is hoped that the intensive studies of the pre-Cambrian of Minnesota and adjacent regions by Professor Goldich and his associates will provide much more detailed data in the near future. An important point will be the absolute ages of these pre-Cambrian iron formations, because this will yield a number of fixes for dates when it may be assumed that the earth still had its anoxygenic atmosphere. The newest work of Goldich *et. al.* (1961) already gives the ages for the main stratigraphical groups but does not contain detailed information about the genesis of the various iron formations found in the Canadian Shield.

The results of Lepp and Goldich are also of interest for our topic in a more direct way, because they note that graphitic slates are commonly associated with the pre-Cambrian iron formations. The carbon content of these graphitic slates is thought to be of biogenic origin, indicating an abundance of primitive forms of life at that early period. This points in the same direction as the vestiges of sulphur bacteria found by Ramdohr in his pyrite grains (Fig. 30). Although real fossils of these early days are still extremely scarce, there is no possible doubt that there was life on earth at those times, in the days when the geologic environment proves the existence of an early anoxygenic atmosphere.

SEDIMENTS FORMED UNDER OXYGENIC ATMOSPHERE: THE RED BEDS

From the studies reviewed above it follows that in properly preserved localities, old sediments may supply indications that they were laid down under reducing atmospheric conditions. The opposite is true too. Sediments may, by the state of their oxidation, indicate that they were formed under an oxygenic atmosphere.

This distinction has, however, to be handled with care. Not every sediment with a few grains of sulphides is indicative of a contemporaneous anoxygenic atmosphere, nor does a sediment formed by grains of oxides automatically proclaim that it was formed under an oxygenic atmosphere. The most common mineral of present-day sands, quartz, for instance, does not give an indication of either an anoxygenic or an oxygenic atmosphere, because it is stable under both types of atmosphere. Also under a reducing atmosphere it is possible that sands are laid down which are so well classified, that is so well sorted out during transportation in rivers or oceans, that all heavier grains, like the sulphides, were laid down separately elsewhere in the river bed or on the ocean bottom, resulting in the formation of pure quartz sands.

For the purpose of recognizing an oxygenic atmosphere by its contemporary sediments, the ideal type is the 'red beds'.

Red beds are fine-grained quartz sediments, which are mainly silty; that is, composed of fine material with a grain size situated between that of sands and of clays. They normally carry finer-grained intercalations of clay, and also coarser beds of sands and of conglomerates. The colour, varying between bright red and reddish brown, is due to a small content of iron, normally of a small percentage by weight only. The iron is in the ferric, highly oxidized, state, and mainly present as limonite, $Fe_2O_3 . n \ H_2O$. This is the common iron mineral formed during superficial, oxidative weathering. Red beds were formed mainly in ancient deserts and are comparable to similar deposits now forming in existing deserts.

We know typical red beds from the 'normal', later geologic history, such as the 'Old Red' of Devonian age and the 'New Red' of Triassic age of Britain, which are some 400 my and 200 my old respectively. There are comparable red beds in the Silurian of North America, some 450 my old, whilst during the Permian system, around 250 my ago, red beds developed quite extensively in many places on earth.

The knowledge gained from present desert formations and from the red beds of the later part of the geologic history can be extrapolated to earlier times. Surprisingly enough at first, but on the other hand quite consistent with our ideas about an early anoxygenic atmosphere, we find that there are no really old red beds.

There are pre-Cambrian deposits of red beds. But, just as with most pre-Cambrian fossils, these belong to late pre-Cambrian times. The Torridonian sandstones of Scotland and the Jotnian sandstones of Fennoskandinavia form a case in point. Both are pre-Cambrian in age, but both belong to that late pre-Cambrian orogenetic cycle, to which also the lower Paleozoic belongs. They belong to the same sequence, and although they seem to be quite different from the Cambrian by their lack of fossils, they are not, in fact, much older.

Neither the Torridonian sandstones, nor the Jotnian sandstones, in which the Dala sandstones form perfect red beds, are well dated. But accepting an age of 600 my for the base of the Cambrian, we can safely ascertain the age of the pre-Cambrian red beds to be less than 1000 my; less than one billion years.

It is quite possible that older red beds occur, and it even ought to be an object of further research into the geological aspects of the origin of life to try to arrive at a dating of the oldest red beds. However, up till now dates older than 1 billion years for red beds do not seem very reliable. I will give two examples, both of the Canadian old shield. Around lake Athabasca, in western Canada, much older red beds have been described. This results, however, from confusion of the much older, well dated, rocks of the basement with the much younger red beds, that are even of paleozoic age

(Gussow, 1959). The other instance is from the Labrador geosyncline in central Canada, where Gastil and others quite recently reported the occurrence of red beds, older than the so-called Grenville orogeny, which is dated at around 1 billion years (Gastil *et al.,* 1960, p. 25). These particular red beds, however, occur outside the area of the Grenville orogeny, which makes correlation extremely difficult.

Just as with the tentative dates given for the sediments formed under an anoxygenic atmosphere, we can consequently also give only a tentative age for the oldest red beds. In a very general way this is one billion years.

PPOVISIONAL DATING OF TRANSITION BETWEEN THE
TWO ATMOSPHERES

The tentative age of 1 billion years for the oldest red beds gives us a provisional minimum age for the present oxygenic atmosphere. On the other hand, a tentative age of 2 billion years could be established for the youngest sediments known to be deposited under an anoxygenic atmosphere. This is the lowest age we can assign up to now for such an atmosphere still to be present on earth.

Concluding this chapter, we may thus for the present state provisionally that from a study of sediments formed in the early history of the earth, geology supplies the following evidence.

Before 2 billion years ago, and at least up to that time, the atmosphere of the earth was anoxygenic and did not contain free oxygen. Life on earth and exogenic processes in geology were pre-actualistic, at least up to that time.

From 1 billion years ago at least the atmosphere was oxygenic. Life on earth and exogenic processes in geology were actualistic, at least from that date onward.

Between 2 billion years and 1 billion years ago the transition between the early anoxygenic to the present oxygenic atmosphere took place. We do not know when this transition actually occurred, but we may confidently expect that further studies will define this period more narrowly. Neither do we know how long this transition itself took in absolute time, say in years or millions of years. We suppose, however, that it was a gradual transition; a slow change, which might have taken a period of considerable length, even when compared with the length of time other major processes in geology take.

TYPE OF GEOLOGICAL EVIDENCE DRAWN FROM FOSSILS AND
FROM THE ENVIRONMENT

If we now compare our findings from the last two chapters, we observe a wide variation between the kinds of evidence geology is able to supply. We have distinguished between three groups: real fossils, biogenic deposits, and evidence drawn from the environment, from contemporary exogenic processes.

Fossils tell us not only that there was life on earth at that time, but also what kind of life.

Biogenic deposits, either the limestone crusts described by MacGregor, or the graphitic slates of Lepp and Goldich; either the microscopical biogenic spots in pyrite grains pictured by Ramdohr, or the big reefs of lime-secreting Algae of the type of *Collenia,* tell us only in a very general way that there was life on earth during that period.

But neither the fossils nor the biogenic deposits tell us anything about the metabolism of life of their time; that is, whether this was oxygenic or anoxygenic. An answer to the latter question can only be drawn from the study of the environment of early life. Only from certain special types of ancient deposits, formed by contemporaneous exogenic processes, can conclusions be drawn about the character of the ancient atmosphere, *i.e.* if this was oxygenic or anoxygenic.

CHAPTER IX

MISCELLANEOUS GEOLOGICAL CONSIDERATIONS

GENERAL

Apart from fossils and other indications of early life on earth, and apart from the character of the environment which can be deduced from contemporary exogenic geologic processes, there are several other considerations which also have a bearing on the study of the origin of life on earth. Fossils and biogenic deposits, and also the environment, were studied in the two preceding chapters. This chapter is reserved for those additional, miscellaneous topics.

First, the importance of clays and quartz for a selective growth of some of the 'organic' compounds during those earliest days of inorganic photosynthesis. Another topic is to enquire whether there possibly has ever been enough carbon dioxide in the early atmosphere for organic photosynthesis to be able to produce our present amount of free oxygen: or conversely, where all the carbon is which has been produced by organic photosynthesis over the last billion years at least. We will have to inquire if geochemistry can answer these questions by drawing up quantitative global estimates of certain elements. Then follows a discussion on the apparent stability of the temperature of the earth over the last couple of billion years. During that time it was never so hot or so cold all over the earth that the protein-based life which had formed earlier was extinguished. At the end of this chapter a few remarks have been added, not on geology itself, but on the danger of a certain type of scientific reasoning which now crops up. That is a form of comparative biochemistry that tries to determine which is 'oldest' or more primitive. Geologists well remember the comparative anatomy which was the fashion during the first half of this century, and which used much the same line of reasoning as comparative biochemistry tends to do now. Paleontological evidence has shown how easily even the most obvious

deductions of comparative anatomy can lead to false conclusions
because the historical development had been different. This warns
us against accepting similar lines of thought in comparative biochemistry.

THE IMPORTANCE OF CLAYS

Clay is one of the most abundant rock types at present on the surface of the earth, and from what we know of the oldest sediments
laid down in early pre-Cambrian times, it will have been about as
abundant then. Clays are very fine-grained rocks. They are formed
by a group of related minerals, the clay minerals, which are all of
a similar build, being formed by silicates of aluminium, with much
water and various other cations, and with a decidedly flaky structure.
They resemble muscovite, both in chemical composition and in the
structure of their crystal lattice, but the individual crystals are of
much smaller size. Their crystal lattice consists of well-defined, thin,
parallel layers of strongly bounded ions, separated by voids in which
only a few hydroxyl groups or cations are found (Fig. 33). The
distance between the individual parallel layers of the lattice can vary
strongly, depending on the number of ions incorporated in the voids.

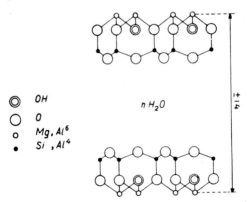

Fig. 33. Schematic section of the crystal lattice of montmorillonite, one
of the clay minerals. Each layer of silicate is separated by a loosely
bound number of water molecules, through which the clay swells when
wetted and shrinks when drying. Maximum distance between silicate
layers is about 14 Å (from Bijvoet *et al.*, 1948).

Clays may have been important in two ways. The extremely small size of the individual grains results in a very large grain surface by weight of a clay sample. This enables strong adsorption on these surfaces of the various compounds of the 'thin soup'. Moreover, the clay crystal lattice forms miniature piles for any diffusing process transversely to its parallel layers. Just as the piles in technology, they might have accentuated differentiation processes. Differential diffusion of a very minor value through a single layer may have become important when summed up over the entire crystal, small as they are.

Differential adsorption of the surface of clay grains and differential diffusion through crystal lattices forming its miniature piles consequently may have been significant in the early days of inorganic photosynthesis. Of course, we do not know of such processes, but because there is a fair probability that they have occurred somehow, it is well to remember that clays were abundant at that time.

THE IMPORTANCE OF QUARTZ

A similar case is presented by the common mineral quartz, which forms the grains of almost all sands now. Although in the early atmosphere other sands were present, as we saw in the preceding chapter, quartz was a very common mineral too; already in the earliest time of the geologic history. The importance of the prevalence of quartz on the surface of the earth lies in the fact that all present living matter is optically active. This fact, first discovered by Louis Pasteur, has since been confirmed by all later studies.

Terent'ev and Klabunovskii (1960) and Klabunovskii (1960) published papers on this subject in the Moscow Symposium, to which the reader is referred for full information. Let it suffice to state here that quartz, with its slightly asymmetrical crystal lattice, has an optically active crystal surface. By selective adsorption of compounds which have optically active molecules, but are inactive because the latter are present on a fifty-fifty basis, optically active compounds can be formed. In nature, however, there probably are as many *dextro*-surfaces of quartz grains as there are *laevo*-surfaces. Consequently, the optical activity of quartz surface in itself is not sufficient to bring about optical separation. There is a probability, however, of a selective natural process operating on this interaction of early 'organic' compounds with optically active surfaces of quartz grains. This is the fact that the sunlight, after having passed through the atmosphere, shows right circular polarization. Theoretically a selective destruction of *dextro*-forms of early 'organic' compounds in the 'thin soup' by the sunlight seems possible. This would leave us with a predominance of *laevo*-active forms, leading to early life.

Again, we do not know the actual processes. The optical activity, and other elements of asymmetry present in modern life are, however, difficult to visualize without complicated reaction chains of the type indicated above. In these reactions the availability of the optically active surfaces of quartz grains, present everywhere, may well have been of great consequence.

GEOCHEMICAL INVENTORIES

As has been remarked in the introductory lines to this chapter, there is yet quite a different branch of natural science that may be drawn upon to find arguments for or against the new theories concerning the origin of life through natural causes. This is geochemistry. Geochemistry draws up global estimates for the abundance of certain elements of the earth's crust.

It is from such global inventories that formal conclusions might be drawn. The best example for our problem is the presence of free oxygen in our atmosphere. Earlier astronomical theories explained this fact by assuming a dissociation of water into hydrogen and oxygen. There is water enough available in the oceans. Its quantity is even so vast that the loss through dissociation to form all present free atmospheric oxygen would hardly be noticed. In this view, the hydrogen formed by dissociation would have escaped from the atmosphere into space, whilst the heavier oxygen had been retained. In contrast, we now postulate a biogenic origin of this same quantity of oxygen formed through dissociation of carbon dioxide. Is this at all possible? Has there ever been sufficient carbon dioxide present in the atmosphere and hydrosphere to supply all this free oxygen? And what happened to the carbon fixed by the plants, produced at the same time the free oxygen was released? Is the amount of fossil carbon, both in coal and oil, anywhere near comparable to the free oxygen formed? Geochemistry, in theory, should be able to supply the answers to these questions.

Now the trouble with geochemical inventories always is that they rest on quite a number of assumptions of a rather hypothetical character. We know only the constitution of the uppermost level of the crust, through oilwells and mines, up to a couple of kilometers. Old cores of eroded mountain chains may give us an insight into the local constitution of parts of the crust which were formerly buried perhaps as deep as 30 km. But global inventories must use rather far-stretched extrapolations from these meagre data. The structure and the composition of the crust under the continents and the oceans is, for instance, very different at present. A geochemical inventory will therefore differ accordingly, if the author adheres to one of a group of theories which postulates permanence of oceans and continents, or if he accepts the possibility of large parts of the continents foundering to oceanic depths.

Geochemistry consequently is not in a position to give well founded answers to many of the question marks it ought, in theory, be able to answer. I will follow here a recent summary by Engelhardt (1959), which is based on the assumption of a certain permanence of oceans and continents.

According to Engelhardt the question about the quantity of carbon dioxide present in atmosphere and hydrosphere cannot be answered by geochemistry. The reason is that carbon dioxide does not form a closed system on the surface of the earth. There is constant injection of carbon dioxide into the atmosphere from volcanic activity. It is one of the commonest gases, not only during eruptions proper, but also during the decline of volcanic activity, and in hot springs and fumaroles. Its rate of production through volcanic activity has, however, not even been estimated with any reliability at present. Far less do we know of its production in the geological past. The only thing we know is that there have been strong variations in volcanic activity in geologic history. Hence we may assume that the volcanic production of carbon dioxide has been sufficient to account for the free oxygen present now, but we have no data upon which to base an inventory.

We have had more luck with the other side of the process: the production of carbon by the plants during organic photosynthesis. After careful consideration of the amount of fossil carbon present in the sediments of the crust of the earth, Engelhardt reaches the conclusion that its order of magnitude is compatible with the assumption that all free oxygen found now is biogenic in origin.

The answers from geochemistry, it must be concluded, are extremely disappointing and not of a hight degree of certainty. They are, however, the best we can offer at present, and they have been very carefully considered. It is a comforting thought that at least they do not contradict the modern theory on the biogenic origin of free oxygen, which is one of the pivots on which the modern view on the origin of life on earth rests. As was the case with other points mentioned earlier in this book, we have no proof, but we are fortunate enough not to be flatly contradicted.

UNIFORMITY OF SURFACE TEMPERATURE OF THE EARTH

We now come to yet another aspect in relation to the history of life on earth; namely, the remarkable uniformity in temperature on the surface of the earth over 2 or 3 billion years at least during which there was well developed life. This is not so much a question directly related to the origin of life, but it has made possible its conservation, and its evolution.

It is, nevertheless, vital to us. For if at some moment during these 2 to 3 billion years a catastrophe had occurred exterminating life on earth, the whole process would have to have been repeated, before there arose anew the possibility of life on earth. That is to say, that all early processes of inorganic photosynthesis, plus those of subsequent selective ascendancy and so forth would have to develop once more. The various selective processes, however, are the result of so many independent variables, such as mutations and environmental factors, that the eventual outcome of such a repetition would certainly have been quite different from the former pattern. Even if it so happened that the same types of biochemistry would become established, the morphological expression of such a second cycle of development of life would certainly have been quite different from the present one.

Consequently this question of a constant temperature of the surface of the earth is of great moment. If this had not been so, we would not have been here to contemplate our distant origin. Apart from that, it is, of course, important also in relation to speculations about life on other planets, either belonging to our own or to other solar systems. It there is life on other planets, circumstances there also ought not only to have permitted some sort of comparable inorganic reactions leading to proto-life of some sort, but on top of that they also must have been of a nature constant enough to permit subsequent preservation, and, of course, evolution, of that particular form of life on its heavenly body.

On our own earth, to return to our subject, our type of life has been protein-based over at least 2 billion years. Now protein is a subtle substance. It survives neither freezing nor heating over any geologic length of time. It follows that over these 2 billion years the mean yearly temperature of the surface of the earth cannot have varied more than a score of degrees centigrade. Or, in other words, over this period it has been remarkably stable.

This pronouncement may well be in need of qualification for the general reader, who, by familiarity with normal geologic literature, has perhaps become convinced of the strong variations in temperature in the geologic past, leading, for instance, to the Ice Ages.

It is true, of course, that there were Ice Ages in the past. Presumably even now we do not live in a postglacial age but in an interglacial period between the last Ice Age and the next one. A future Ice Age may well be expected for geologic reasons, although, incidentally, it might be possible that man prevents its coming, willingly or even unwillingly, through an excess of industrialization.

So, there have been Ice Ages, several of them occurred in the recent geological past, over the last million years or so. Others occurred further back, between 200 million and 250 million years ago, during late Carboniferous and early Permian systems. Still other Ice Ages are known to have occurred in late pre-Cambrian times, probably around 600 million years ago. There are, moreover, almost certainly still older Ice Ages, still less known. As a counterpart to these Ice Ages, there have been warmer periods too. These are far more difficult to detect geologically, but one might well speak of Heat Ages. As an example, let us cite the late Permian, when, closely following upon the early Permian Ice Age, a Heat Age produced such strong evaporation in many parts of the earth that most of our primary rock-salt deposits were formed at that time.

So there have repeatedly been Ice Ages in the geological past, whilst, although less well known, there also have been Heat Ages.

But what does this mean? Ice Ages and Heat Ages indicate strong, regional, climatic variations. But they indicate strong climatic variations for part of the earth only. None of the latest Ice Ages changed the tropics to any extent. Neither the tropical rain forest nor the central zone of the coral seas was affected. Ice Ages and Heat Ages did not affect all of the earth. Never did the whole surface of the earth freeze over or become unbearably hot. Ice Ages held sway in higher latitudes, in what are now polar and temperate regions. Heat Ages predominantly affected lower latitudes, such as the present tropical and subtropical regions. Ice Ages and Heat Ages are the result of a lowering or a rising of the mean global annual temperature over less than ten degrees centrigrade only.

So, to conclude, notwithstanding the occurrence of Ice Ages or Heat Ages, the mean temperature of the surface of the earth showed only very slight variations over that period of 2 billion years. Now the important thing is that this period represents an extreme length of time, even if measured against the long times normal in geology and astronomy.

GLASSHOUSE EFFECT OF THE ATMOSPHERE

The mean temperature at the surface of the earth is the sum of a number of independant variables, the most important being solar radiation, heat flow from the interior of the earth, and heat retention by the atmosphere. Each of these is in itself complex.

Solar radiation is the main heat source for the surface of the earth. Now it seems pretty well established that apart from sunspot cycles and such minor variations, solar radiation has been extremely constant. Not only has it been very constant over the short time of some hundred years or so during which meteorologists have actually measured solar radiation, but it seems quite certain that it must also have been constant over lengths of time of several billion years. The simple nuclear reactions generating heat in the sun are reasonably well understood by now, and can be calculated and extrapolated back into time with relative ease. So if we take account only of the solar radiation, a constant mean temperature of the earth's surface is not so amazing at all.

The heat flow from the earth's interior, on the other hand, is very imperfectly known. It may have shown important fluctuations in the past for all we know. We can do no more than put on record that its variations have never been so excessive as to endanger the continuation of life on earth.

The fact is that climatologists find it difficult to explain even minor changes in mean temperature, such as have led to the last Ice Ages. This stems from the fact that the heat retention of our atmosphere is a very complex factor, possessing various feedback mechanisms which counteract either cooling or heating by variations in the primary factors of heat flow.

For example, a warming of the earth's surface either by stronger solar radiation or by a greater heat flow from the interior, would lead to increased evaporation, and hence to more cloud formation. This would in its turn directly affect the reflectivity of the atmosphere, the so-called albedo of the earth, resulting in a smaller part of the solar radiation reaching the surface of the earth. Other, more complex, variations, such as a shift in altitude of the tropopause, would also enter into the process, all tending to buffer the effect of any primary variation in solar radiation or terrestrial heat flow.

Consequently, climatologists are busily studying the mechanism which could have led to such minor variations in mean temperature through which Ice Ages originated. They are not so much concerned with the reasons why, even over the long periods of geologic history, no stronger variations have occurred which could possibly have been obnoxious to life on earth.

Shapley (1953), for instance, gives six conditions for planetary life, four of which directly apply to our problem. These are:

1. 'The controlling star must not be variable by more than 4 or 5 per cent; it must not be a double star and, of course, not subject to catastrophic explosions like those of the novae.' It follows that our controlling Sun has followed these conditions for the last several billion years at least.

2. 'The orbital eccentricity of the planet must be low, to avoid excessive differences in insolation as the planet moves from perihelion to aphelion and back (most cometary orbits would be lethal for organisms).'

3. 'The planet must have a suitable rotation period, so that nights do not overcool, nor days overheat.' Our planet Earth accordingly

has sensibly followed the latter two prescriptions also over the last several billion years.

4. 'Water, the practical solvent for living processes, must be available in liquid form. The kind of life we are talking about and thinking of does not live in uncondensing steam or unmelting ice. The basic requirement, therefore, is that the living planet must be at a proper distance from its star, — in the liquid-water belt — not as close as Mercury is to the Sun, nor as remote as Jupiter.'

It follows that these four assumptions have held true over the greater part at least of geologic history. Apart from the astronomical position of the planet Earth on an intermediate orbit around its controlling star, this arises mainly from the constancy of solar radiation. Any variations in other heat flows, such as variation of terrestrial heat flow, or the hypothetical temporary shielding by stellar dust clouds, appear to have been largely counteracted by the buffering of our atmosphere. The heat retention by the atmosphere, with its feedback mechanisms, seems to be able to temper effectively any possible primary variations in heat flow. It follows that our atmosphere is a very good glasshouse indeed, a fact which has played a major role in the evolution of life on earth. In view of the fact that this quality of our atmosphere mainly rests with its water vapour, which will have been present in the primeval atmosphere too, we may assume that this glasshouse effect already occurred in the early days of the origin of life on earth.

THE DANGERS OF COMPARATIVE BIOCHEMISTRY

As a final remark in this chapter, I should like to add a digression not so much about facts, but about the way in which these facts have been used in some scientific reasoning. In other words, I want to warn against a certain type of deduction drawn from comparative biochemistry that one meets more and more in biological papers on the origin of life on earth.

The basic assumption of this reasoning is that what is more simple in metabolism, biochemically, is more primitive and consequently older in the history of life. This assumption is entirely unjustified. It has never been tested, and will be very difficult to test. Also, quite possibly, it is false.

Geology has seen similar reasoning in comparative anatomy, where 'simple' has also been largely confused with 'primitive' and with 'early'. Many have been the trees of evolution in which members of parallel or converging evolutionary lines have been mixed, often accompanied by an absolute disregard for the stratigraphical position, *i.e.* the relative age of those forms. Imaginary forefathers were supposed to have sired entirely non-related offspring, sometimes tens of millions of years their older, not because of paleontological proof of paternity, but only because they looked 'simpler'. The tenet that 'no-one can be forefather to someone older than himself' has even had to be applied rather forcefully to cope with this trend in comparative anatomy.

In the history of the vertebrates, for instance, marine animals, fishes, were the earliest known, whilst later less simple forms conquered the land. But that does not mean that we have to take the whale, seal and seacow as being more primitive than other mammals, and relegate them to the evolutionary trend of the present-day fish. This is, of course, a crude example, but the type of reasoning mentioned above really is not so very much different. In research into the possible origin of life through natural causes, there is at present a similar tendency. Several of the anaerobic microbes with simple metabolism are taken and arranged in ascending order in primeval time. But this is the same as taking the whale, seal and seacow and proclaiming these to be the most ancient mammals.

There is even no proof that our present anaerobic bacteriae are that ancient at all. Quite possibly they developed much later from actualistic aerobic life, just as the seagoing mammals mentioned returned to the oceans long after their ancestors had made the evolutionary stride from sea to land. 'Simple' is no proof either for 'primitive' or 'early', and arranging our present-day anaerobic bacteria in such an ascending order gives the false impression that we know much more about the origin of life than we actually do.

Chapter X

THE ORIGIN OF LIFE AND ITS LATER EVOLUTION

EVOLUTION AND PALEONTOLOGY

At the tail end of the discussions in this book, it is well, I think, to stress once more the distinction between the origin of life and its early development on the one hand, and its later evolution on the other. Geologists today feel safe in stating that paleontology has proven the existence of natural evolution over the last half-billion years. This scientific faith does not stem so much from the fact that we know all about evolution. The contrary is even true, and many and varied are still the gaps in the paleontological record, both as regards the bridging of deviating structures in different groups of plants and animals, and the gaps caused by barren layers intercalated between fossiliferous strata. Nevertheless, we do have this faith, and this assumption is largely based on the evolution of our knowledge of the paleontological record, since the time when theories of evolution became first enunciated. It is due to the fact that the many lucky discoveries of linkages which were missing up to that time, always confirm, be it in a general way, the theory of evolution.

Of course, in detail, parentages have had to be shifted. Also, of course, there have in reality always been more different kinds of plants and animals in the past than we know of from the fossil records. Every new find adds to our knowledge, and it follows that evolution has often been more complicated in reality than had been surmised by a paleontologist drawing ideal ancestry lines too much schematized from too scanty a material. But although there have been revisions in detail, the main lines of evolution became confirmed whenever some link still missing was actually found.

All of this applies, however, only to the later evolution of life on earth, to the period from which we have a paleontological record.

That is, approximately, to the last half-billion years, from the Cambrian system onwards. As stated above, this period is not only much shorter, but also much later than that in which the origin of life and its early beginnings took place. Nevertheless, the two are often treated together, the findings of later evolution are extrapolated backwards in an unpermissable way, and the distinction between the two is often ignored in the literature.

SEVEN ASSUMPTIONS

As a case in point let me cite the very recent and authoritative book by Kerkut (1960), who, in a thoughtful essay, takes a delightfully critical attitude towards evolution. Kerkut maintains that the theory of evolution is based on seven assumptions, which together form the 'General Theory of Evolution'. These assumptions are (Kerkut, 1960, p. 6):

1. Non-living things gave rise to living material, *i.e.* spontaneous generation occurred *.

2. Spontaneous generation occurred only once.
   (The other assumptions, according to Kerkut, all follow from the second one.)

3. Viruses, bacteria, plants and animals are all interrelated.

4. Protozoa gave rise to Metazoa.

5. The various invertebrate phyla are interrelated.

6. The invertebrates gave rise to the vertebrates.

7. Within the vertebrates, the fish gave rise to the amphibia, the amphibia to the reptiles, and the reptiles to the birds and mammals.

---

* As stated before, I do not think the usage of the phrase 'spontaneous generation' to be a happy one in this context. On p. 7 of his work Kerkut uses the word 'biogenesis', an expression coined, I believe, by Bernal, as a synonym. Biogenesis will be used here also to denote transition from non-living to living.

The first two assumptions quoted deal with the origin of life on earth, the next five with its later evolution. Hence they are not comparable in scope and they form the latest example to my knowledge, where origin and later evolution of life have been confused.

Kerkut's last five assumptions consequently fall outside the scope of this book. For the sake of completeness a few more remarks have, however, to be added.

The objections raised against these five assumptions have, I think, been answered before in modern treatises on evolution. The reader may be referred, for instance, to Simpson (1949). It must be pointed out, however, that even within these five assumptions 3 to 6 are not at all on the same footing as number 7. Perhaps one had better say that some fish gave rise to amphibia, some reptiles to mammals and birds, because on the one hand only some definite, narrowly defined, structural groups within the earlier phyla led to the higher organization, whilst on the other hand a polyphyletic origin of these higher phyla remains quite possible. Stated in this way, however, assumption 7 is based on fact, *i.e.* on paleontological records, whereas assumptions 3—6 are theories based only on similarities within the present flora and fauna, but without any support from the historical paleontological record.

But let us return to assumptions 1 and 2. The gist of what we learned is that, according to a theory widely accepted by biologists, organic material arose by inorganic processes and that non-living matter subsequently developed into living. The facts gleaned from geology make it probable that the environment postulated by that theory, *i.e.* the anoxygenic atmosphere, has indeed been present. This is not, of course, proof that biogenesis occurred. It only proves the feasibility of that theory, and so it justifies the postulation of assumption 1.

Kerkut's second assumption, to my mind, does not do sufficient justice to all the possibilities in biogenesis. Even if similar inorganic photosynthetic reactions gave rise, say, at the same time but in different localities, to similar organic material, whilst subsequently non-living matter gave rise to living along some, or even along many, parallel lines, we would, I think, still call such primitive life interrelated. In the same way we call mammals interrelated, although there is a possibility of polyphyletic origin of different evolutionary lines within the phylum from different, but nearly related, lines of mammal-like reptiles. Perhaps I allow the ideas of the practical historian in geology to prevail too much over pure philosophical reason. But to my mind we shall never be able to prove whether biogenesis occurred only once or was multiple. As long as the results are comparable, and as long as they are brought about by a comparable history, the use of the word 'related' is justified.

POSSIBILITY OF MULTIPLE BIOGENESIS

It follows that assumption 2, that biogenesis occurred only once, is unnecessary. Moreover, we can make a case against it, and assume that it was multiple. We have found that geologic history works with extremely long periods, during which cumulation of small effects may eventually lead to large consequences. We have noted the probability of a very long period in the early history of life during which there was coexistence of the inorganic photosynthetic reactions leading to the 'organic' materials of the 'thin soup', of proto-life and of early life.

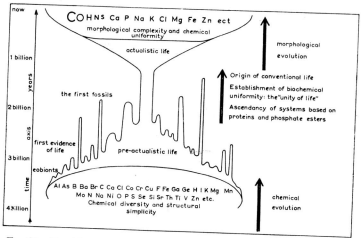

Fig. 34. Simplified presentation of the origin and the development of life on earth. The Pirie drawing (compare Fig. 14) redrawn according to the geological aspects of the origin of life on earth.

Quite possibly life will have developed in many different ways and at many different dates during this period. But natural selection will have been very strong during the period of transition to the oxygenic atmosphere. It may then have played upon this wide field of possible life forms, eventually narrowing it down to the beginning of our later life. This has been schematized in a re-drawn version of Pirie's double cone (Fig. 34).

All this, of course, is mere hypothesis. It is, however, the sort of hypothesizing which logically follows from observed facts, and, moreover, it is not in conflict with the known facts of the geological records. It is, on the other hand, to return to the starting point of this chapter, quite a different thing than the study of the later evolution of life on earth, which, for all shell-bearing or skeleton-bearing animals, is based on the facts of the paleontological record.

CHAPTER XI

CONCLUSIONS

WHAT WE KNOW

The factual conclusions from our study of the geological aspects of the origin of life on earth have been summarized in Fig. 36. Fig. 35 is a companion figure, for comparison with Fig. 36. Fig. 35 is taken from the American paleontologist and stratigrapher Raymond C. Moore (1958) and shows what geology is normally interested in, *i.e.* the study of the history of the earth, datable by the fossil record. Detailed information of this kind practically begins at the base of the Paleozoic, with the Cambrian system. Nine out of ten of the phyla of the animal kingdom were already represented in the Cambrian system. Very little, on the other hand, is known about earlier periods, and all ancestry lines during this time are dotted, with the exception of that of the microbes. Moreover, at about 1200 my ago, everything originates from nebulous beginnings.

In Fig. 36 Moore's picture is re-drawn on another scale to emphasize those earlier periods of the history of the earth. From this picture it follows immediately how relatively short the time since the beginning of the Paleozoic is, when compared to the time life has existed on earth. There are no nebulous beginnings around 1200 my ago, but we have real fossils of some 1600 my ago, and even much older indications of the presence of life on earth.

Apart from the fossils and para-fossils, there are definite indications that the earth had an anoxygenic atmosphere of reducing character, certainly up to 2 billion years ago. Some of the indications we have

Fig. 35. Evolution of life on earth, as schematized by R. C. Moore (1958). Main divisions of plants and animals and their evolutionary development in the course of time are shown. Times of some important orogenetic periods in North America are posted at the left.

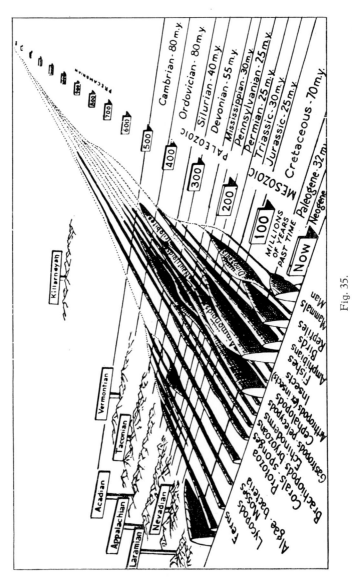

Fig. 35.

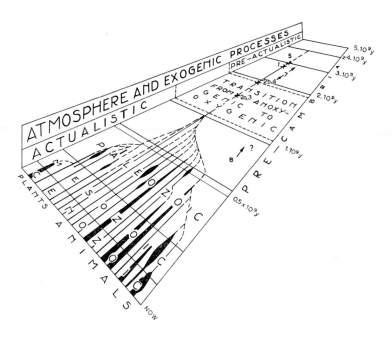

Fig. 36. Schematic history of life on earth. 1. Biogenic lime secretions
from South Africa, described by MacGregor. 2a. Earliest true fossils,
described from Canada by Tyler and Barghoorn. 2b. Anoxygenic Blind
River deposits, described from Canada by Ramdohr. 3. *Collenia* type
algal reefs from Africa, described by Gravelle and Lelubre. 4. Non-
oxidized rocks from Finland, described by Rankama. 5. Anoxygenic
Dominion Reef deposits from South Africa, described by Ramdohr.
7. Anoxygenic iron formations, described from Canada and Montana,
by Lepp and Goldich. 8. Approximate age of earliest red beds. For
geographical location of numbers 1 to 7, compare Fig. 15.

of the existence of life on earth are older, so we do have evidence
of the existence of early, anoxygenic life on earth.

Our present oxygenic atmosphere was already established about
one billion years ago. It was somewhere between the two dates of
two billion years — for which we have the as yet youngest indication
of an anoxygenic atmosphere — and one billion years — that of the
earliest deposits known up to now to have originated under an
oxygenic atmosphere — that the transition from early anoxygenic
to the present oxygenic atmosphere took place.

This transition is in all probability due to organic activity. Free
oxygen was formed by organisms which had aquired the ability of
assimilating carbon and producing free oxygen through the dissociation of carbon dioxide by organic photosynthesis. It was only after
primitive life had aquired this new kind of metabolism that anything
like our present plant kingdom could become established on earth.
The animal kingdom is, of course, still younger, although perhaps
only slightly so, because it scavenges the carbon transformed to organic substances by plants by organic photosynthesis, a process of
which animals are incapable.

The animal kingdom was, however, already well established in
late pre-Cambrian times. In a general way, consequently, not only
the transition from the primeval anoxygenic atmosphere to the actual
oxygenic one took place somewhere in that period between two
billion and one billion years, but also the subsequent development of
the early ancestors of both our present plant and animal kingdoms.

WHAT WE SHALL NEVER KNOW

After this enumeration of the facts we have about the early history
of life on earth, we may well inquire what type of question we shall
presumably never be able to answer. We shall, for instance, never
know with any certainty the exact nature of these early inorganic
processes of photosynthesis which are thought to have produced the
organic material in the 'thin soup'. These compounds will not have
had any distinctive morphological form, and it is only by their morphology, by their outline, that fossils can be recognized as such.

Nor can we ever hope to have a detailed account of the evolution
of that early life which followed upon, and most probably was even
contemporaneous with, the later part of the purely inorganic growth

of 'organic' molecules. We might find fossilized, structurally preserved, parts of this early life, just as we have now found deposits
formed by such life. But the fossil material will always be extremely
scanty. We will, at the most, have a fossil here, another there, but
never enough to permit the construction of evolutionary lines comparable to those we have established for the later evolution of the
higher life forms of more complex morphological structure.

WHAT FURTHER RESEARCH MAY TEACH US

It is to be hoped that further research will bring us more of those
valuable discoveries of early fossils, be they from the primeval pre-
actualistic period or from the dawn of our present life. By such
lucky finds it will in future be possible to furnish a much more
substantial documentation of early life than we have at present.

Moreover, we may legitimately hope that more intensive mapping
of the Old Shields will yield better correlations between the series
of rocks by which they are built up. With the availability of more
absolute datings it will then be possible to assign more reliable
absolute ages to these fossil finds, both old and new.

Another conceivable result of future research, a result very important to my mind, will be that more will be known about the
environment of early life. If we have more places where sediments
can be said to have formed either under primeval anoxygenic or
under the present oxygenic atmospheric conditions, and if such
localities could be dated more reliably, it would be possible to define
more narrowly the time of transition from the primeval to the present
atmosphere.

If we could some day arrive at an estimate of the time this transition actually took, this would in turn give us some idea of the actual
rate of biogenic production of free oxygen; of great value, of course,
to biologists interested in the rate of metabolism of early life.

CLOSING REMARK

Having thus summarized what we know, what we shall never know,
and what we hope further research will teach us in years to come,
we may arrive at a final conclusion. This is that the findings of
geology are in complete agreement with the modern biological views

on an origin of life on earth through natural causes. Although, of course, such an agreement offers no proof that the newer biological theories are correct, at least it offers us a most pleasant ending to our studies into one of the most intriguing problems of present-day science

REFERENCES

AHRENS, L. H., 1955. Oldest rocks exposed. *Geol. Soc. Am., Spec. Paper* 62 : 155-168.

AULT, W. U., 1959. Isotopic fractionaticn in geochemical processes. In : P. H. ABELSON (Editor), *Researches in Geochemistry*. Wiley and Sons, New York, pp. 241-259.

BERNAL, J. D., 1949. The physical basis of life. *Proc. Phys. Soc. (London)*, A, 62 : 537-558 ; B, 62 : 597-618.

— 1959. The problem of stages in biopoesis. In : A. I. OPARIN (Editor), *The Origin of Life on Earth*. IUB Symposium Series, Vol. I, Pergamon Press, London, pp. 38-53.

BIJVOET, J. M., KOLKMEIJER, N. H. and MACGILLAVRY, C. H., 1948. *Röntgenanalyse van Kristallen*. Centen, Amsterdam, 300 pp.

DERRY, D. R., 1959. Evidence of the origin of Blind River uranium deposits — A progress report. *Geol. Soc. Am., Bull.*, 70 : 1587.

ENGELHARDT, W. Freiherr von, 1959. Kreislauf und Entwicklung in der Geschichte der Erdrinde. *Nova Acta Leopoldina*, 21 (143): 85-99.

EPSTEIN, S., 1959. The variations of the O^{18}/O^{16} ratio in nature and some geologic implications. In : P. H. ABELSON (Editor), *Researches in Geochemistry*. Wiley and Sons, New York, pp. 217-240.

FOLINSBEE, R. E., BAADSGAARD, H. and LIPSON, J., 1960. Potassium — argon time scale. In : TH. SORGENFREI (Editor), *Repts. 21st Intern. Geol. Congr., Copenhagen*, 3 : 7-17.

FURON, R., 1960. *Géologie de l'Afrique*. Payot, Paris, 2nd ed., 400 pp.

GASTIL, G., BLAIS, R., KNOWLES, D. M. and BERGERON, R., 1960. The Labrador geosyncline. In : TH. SORGENFREI (Editor), *Repts. 21st Intern. Geol. Congr., Copenhagen*, 9 : 21-38.

GLAESSNER, M., 1961. Pre-Cambrian animals. *Sci. American*, 204 : 72-78.

GOLDICH, S. S. *et al.*, 1961. The Precambrian geology and geochronology of Minnesota. *Minnesota Geol. Surv., Bull.*, 41 : 1-193.

GRAVELLE, M. and LELUBRE, M., 1957. Découverte de Stromatolithes du groupe des Conophyton dans le Pharusien de l'Ahaggar occidental (Sahara Central). *Bull. Soc. géol. France*, 7 : 435-442.

GUSSOW, W. C., 1959. Athabasca formation of Western Canada. *Geol. Soc. Am., Bull.*, 70 : 1-18.

HOOYKAAS, R., 1959. *Natural Law and Divine Miracle*. Brill, Leiden, 237 pp.

HOLMES, A., 1947 a. The construction of a geological time-scale. *Trans. Geol. Soc. Glasgow*, 21 (1): 117-152.

— 1947 b. A revised estimate of the age of the earth. *Nature*, 159: 127-128.

— 1954. The oldest dated minerals of the Rhodesian shield. *Nature*, 173: 612-614.

— 1960. A revised geological time-scale. *Trans. Edinburg Geol. Soc.*, 17: 183-216.

INGERSON, E., 1953. Nonradiogenic isotopes in geology: a review. *Geol. Soc. Am., Bull.*, 64: 301-374.

KERKUT, G. A., 1960. *Implications of Evolution*. Pergamon Press, London, 174 pp.

KLABUNOVSKII, E. I., 1959. Absolute asymmetric synthesis and asymmetric catalysis. In: A. I. OPARIN (Editor), *The Origin of Life on Earth*. IUB Symposium Series, Vol. 1, Pergamon Press, London, pp. 158-168.

KLUYVER, A. J., 1955. Microbe en leven. *Koninkl. Ned. Akad. Wetenschap., Jaarb.* 1954 (5), 27 pp.

KULLERUD, G., 1959. Sulfide systems as geological thermometers. In: P. H. ABELSON (Editor), *Researches in Geochemistry*. Wiley and Sons, New York, pp. 301-335.

KULP, J. L., 1955. Isotopic dating and the geologic time scale. *Geol. Soc. Am., Spec. Paper* 62: 609-630.

— 1960. The geological time scale. In: TH. SORGENFREI (Editor), *Repts. 21st Intern. Geol. Congr., Copenhagen*, 3: 18-27.

LEPP, H. and GOLDICH, S. S., 1959. Chemistry and origin of iron formations. *Geol. Soc. Am., Bull.*, 70: 1637.

LIEBENBERG, W. R., 1960. On the origin of uranium, gold and osmiridium in the conglomerates of the Witwatersrand goldfields. *Neues Jahrb. Mineral., Abhandl.*, 94: 831-867 (Festband Ramdohr, II).

LYELL, C., 1866-68. *Principles of Geology: Being an Enquiry how far the former Changes of the Earth's Surface are referable to Causes now in Operation*. 10th ed., 2 vols., London.

— 1873. *On the Geological Evidences of the Antiquity of Man, with Remarks on Theories of the Origin of Species by Variation*. 4th. ed., London.

MACGREGOR, A. M., 1940. A pre-Cambrian algal limestone in Southern Rhodesia. *Trans. Geol. Soc. S. Africa*, 43: 9-16.

MILLER, S. L., 1959. Formation of organic compounds on the primitive earth. In: A. I. OPARIN (Editor), *The Origin of Life on Earth*.

IUB Symposium Series, Vol. I, Pergamon Press, London, pp. 123-135.

— 1960. Formation of organic compounds on the primitive earth. In : M. FLORKIN (Editor), Aspects of the Origin of Life. Pergamon Press, Oxford, pp. 85-97.

MOORE, R. C., 1958. Introduction to Historical Geology. McGraw-Hill, New York, 2nd ed., 656 pp.

OPARIN, A. I., 1938. The Origin of Life. Dover Publications, New York, 2nd ed., 270 pp.

— (Editor), 1959. The Origin of Life on Earth. Proc. 1st Intern. Symposium Intern. Union Biochem., IUB Symposium Series, Vol. I, Pergamon Press, London, 436 pp.

PIRIE, N. W., 1957. The origins of life. Moscow symposium. Nature, 180 : 886-888.

— 1959. Chemical diversity and the origins of life. In : A. I. OPARIN (Editor), The Origin of Life on Earth. IUB Symposium Series, Vol. I, Pergamon Press, London, pp. 76-83.

POLKANOV, A. A. and GERLING, E. K., 1960. The pre-Cambrian geochronology of the Baltic shield. In : TH. SORGENFREI (Editor), Repts. 21st. Intern. Geol. Congr., Copenhagen, 9 : 183-191.

POSTGATE, J., 1954. The sulphur bacteria. New Biol., 17: 58-76.

RAMDOHR, P., 1958. Die Uran- und Goldlagerstätten Witwatersrand, Blind River District, Dominion Reef, Serra de Jacobina : Erzmikroskopische Untersuchungen und ein geologischer Vergleich. Abhandl. deut. Akad. Wiss. Berlin, Kl. Chem., Geol. u. Biol., 3: 35 + XIX pp.

RANKAMA, K., 1955. Geologic evidence of chemical composition of the Precambrian atmosfere. Geol. Soc. Am., Spec. Paper 62 : 651-664.

RUBEY, W. W., 1955. Development of the hydrosphere and atmosphere, with special reference to probable composition of the early atmosphere. Geol. Soc. Am., Spec. Paper 62 : 631-650.

RUTTEN, M. G., 1957. Origin of life on earth, its evolution and actualism. Evolution, 11: 56-59.

RUSSEL, R. D. and FARQUAR, R. M., 1960. Lead Isotopes in Geology. Interscience, New York-London, 251 pp.

SAPOZHNIKOW, D. J., 1959. Entstehung und Evolution der phototrophen Ernährungsweise. In : A. I. OPARIN (Editor), The Origin of Life on Earth. IUB Symposium Series, Vol. I, Pergamon Press, pp. 635-641.

SHAPLEY, H., 1953. On climate and life. In : H. SHAPLEY (Editor), Climatic Change. Harvard Univ. Press, Cambridge (Mass.), pp. 1-12.

SIMPSON, G. G., 1949. The Meaning of Evolution. Yale Univ. Press. Abridged edition : Mentor Books, New York, 1951, 192 pp.

TERENIN, A. N., 1959. Photosynthesis in the shortest ultraviolet. In : A. I. OPARIN (Editor), *The Origin of Life on Earth*. IUB Symposium Series, Vol. I, Pergamon Press, London, pp. 136-139.

TERENT'EV, A. P. and KLABUNOVSKII, E. I., 1959. The role of dissimetry in the origin of living material. In : A. I. OPARIN (Editor), *The Origin of Life on Earth*. IUB Symposium Series, Vol. I, Pergamon Press, London, pp. 95-105.

TILTON, G. R. and DAVIS, G. L., 1960. Geochronology. In : P. H. ABELSON (Editor), *Researches in Geochemistry*. Wiley and Sons, New York, pp. 190-216.

TYLER, S. A. and BARGHOORN, E. S., 1954. Occurrence of structurally preserved plants in the pre-Cambrian rocks on the Canadian shield. *Science*, 119 : 606-608.

— 1962. Full report to be published by the *Geol. Soc. Am.*, either in the *Bull.* or as *Spec. Paper*.

UREY, H. C., 1951. *The Planets, their Origin and Development*. Yale Univ. Press, New Haven, 245 pp.

WEXLER, H., 1953. Radiation balance of the Earth as a factor in climatic change. In : H. SHAPLEY (Editor), *Climatic Change*. Harvard Univ. Press, Cambridge (Mass.), pp. 73-106.

WILSON, A. T., 1960. Synthesis of macromolecules. *Nature*, 188 : 1007-1009.

WILSON, A. E., 1957. Life in the Proterozoic. In : J. E. GILL (Editor), The Proterozoic of Canada. *Roy. Soc. Canada, Spec. Publ.* 2 : 18-27.

WINKLER, K. C., 1960. Virus mirabile. In : H. W. OBBINK and others, *Leven en Dood*. Bohn, Haarlem, pp. 86-99.

YOUNG, R. B., 1940 a. Further notes on algal structures in the Dolomite Series. *Trans. Geol. Soc. S. Africa*, 43 : 17-22.

— 1940 b. Note on an unusual type of concretionary structure in limestones of the Dolomite Series. *Trans. Geol. Soc. S. Africa*, 43 : 23-26.

ZEUNER, F. E., 1951. *Dating the Past — An Introduction to Geochronology*. Methuen, London, 2nd ed., 493 pp.

INDEX

Actinium-lead decay series, 32, 33
Actualism, 7-10, 12, 14, 18, 19, 42, 65, 66
Actualisme, 7
Aerobic, 47, 62
Age of the earth, 41
Aktualismus, 7
Albedo, 123
Albian, 40
Algae, 70, 75-77, 79, 82, 84, 85, 91, 114
Algonkian, 71
Alps, 8, 11, 13
Amino-acids, 49, 52, 53, 60
Amphibia, 127, 128
Anaerobic, 47, 48, 59, 62, 63, 125
Andes, 13
Appalachians, 8, 11
Aradiatic, 63
Archaeic, 71
Argentine, 100, 102
Assimilation, organic -, 59-61, 63, 134
Atmosphere, actualistic -, 62-65, 70, 82, 91, 133
Atmosphere, anoxygenic -, 48, 49, 60, 62-64, 89, 92, 96, 97, 106, 109-111, 113, 114, 128, 134, 135
Atmosphere, oxygenic -, 47, 58, 60-65, 70, 88, 89, 95, 97, 100, 111, 113, 114, 130, 134, 135

Atmosphere, pre-actualistic -, 62-66, 70, 88, 91, 92, 113, 133
Atmosphere, primeval -, 48, 49, 51, 58, 60, 62-65, 96, 124, 134, 135
Atmosphere, reducing -, 94, 96, 97
Atomic number, 31, 32
Atomic symbol, 31, 32
Atomic weight, 31-34
Augite, 95, 97
Azoic, 71

Bacteria, 59, 105, 111, 125, 127
Bajocian, 40
Barghoorn, E. S. and Tyler, S. A., 6, 87
Basement, 72, 73, 112
Bay of Balae, 16
Bernal, J. D., 127
Bijvoet, J. M., 116
Billion, 6
Biogenesis, 127-129
Bioherm, 77, 91
Biotite, 95
Birds, 127, 128
Blind River, Ontario, 70, 89, 99, 104, 109, 133
Botnian, 97
Bulawayo, Southern Rhodesia, 77-83

Cambrian, 39, 40, 72-75, 77, 92, 112, 127, 131, 132
Campania Napolitana, 15, 18
Cap Blanc Nez, 22
Carbon dioxide, 59-61, 118, 119, 134
Carboniferous, 40, 121
Catastrophes, doctrine of -, 7-10, 12-14, 18, 19
Cellulose, 83
Cenozoic, 24, 39, 133
Chemical diversity of early life, 57, 58, 129
Chemical uniformity of present life, 45, 57, 58, 129
Chert, 83
Chlorophyll, 49
Clay (minerals), 58, 95-97, 111, 115-117
Coal, 118
Coelenterata, 79
Collenia, 89-92
Comparative anatomy, 125
Comparative biochemistry, 115, 124
Cone-in-cone, 83
Conophyton, 89-92
Correlation, stratigraphic -, 22, 71
Creation, 2, 3, 5, 50
Cretaceous, 40, 132
Croixian, 40
Crustaceans, 75

Dala sandstone, 112
Dark minerals, 95
Dating, absolute -, 21, 25, 28-31, 37-39, 71, 78
Dating, relative -, 21-25, 28, 29
Daughter element, 30
Decay, radioactive -, 25-27, 30-33, 37, 106
Deluge, 9, 14

Dendrochronology, 21, 25
Derry, D. R., 109
Desert climate, 95
Desmoinesian, 40
Devonian, 40, 112, 132
Dextro optical activity, 117, 118
Dinosaur track, 12
Dissociation of carbon dioxyde, 59, 61
Dogma, 3
Dolomite series, 77-81, 83
Dominion reef, 70, 99, 109, 133
Dover, 22

Endogenic processes, 64-66, 110
Engelhardt, W., 119
English Channel, 22
Eobiont, 57, 58, 129
Eocene, 40
Erosion, 10, 11, 65, 73, 94-96, 100
Evolution, natural -, 2, 3, 23, 126-128, 130, 131, 134
Exogenic processes, 64-66, 70, 94, 97, 99, 110, 113-115, 133

Feldspar, 95-97
Finland, 97, 98, 133
Fish, 125, 127, 128
Flint, 83
Floods, 14, 18
Fossil carbon, 118, 119
Fungi, 86
Furon, R., 92

Gastil, C., 113
Generatio spontanea, 3, 4, 50, 51, 127
Geochemical inventory, 118, 119
Geosyncline, 65, 72-74
Goldich, S. S., 110

Gold-uranium deposits, 70, 71, 98, 99, 109
Glasshouse effect, 122, 124
Granite, 64, 65, 67, 70, 78, 97, 98
Graphitic slate, 110, 111, 114
Gravelle, M. and Lelubre, M., 6, 70, 77, 89, 90, 133
Greenland, 12
Guadalupian, 40
Gunflint iron formation, 83-89
Gussow, W. C., 113

Heat Age, 121, 122
Heat flow, terrestrial -, 122-124
Helium method of dating, 88
Herculaneum, 15
Himalaya, 13
Hoggar, 89, 90
Holmes, A., 6, 33
Hooykaas, R., 6, 8, 9
Hornblende, 95, 97
Hutton, J., 9

Ice Age, 12, 121-123
Ice-cap, 12
Igneous rocks, 24, 25, 28-30, 77
Ilmenite, 99
Index fossil, 23, 28
India, 72
Indus valley, 96
Infra-Cambrian, 91
Inorganic synthesis of 'organic' compounds, 46, 48, 49, 60
Invertebrates, 127
Iron formations, 70, 83, 85, 109, 110, 133
Iron ore veins, 109, 110
Iron, ferric -, 97, 98, 111
Iron, ferrous -, 97, 98, 111
Isostatic equilibrium, 11
Isotope, 25, 26, 30-38

Isotope dilution, 36

Jotnian, 112
Jurassic, 40, 109, 132

Kerkut, G. A., 127, 128
Klabunovskii, E. I., 117
Kluyver, A. J., 1, 76, 82
Kola Peninsula, 41
Kulp, J. L., 39-41

Labrador geosyncline, 113
Laevo optical activity, 117, 118
Lake Athabasca, 112
Lake Superior, 70, 109
Lateritisation, 110
Lead age, concordant -, 37
Lead-lead method of absolute dating, 37, 38
Lead, nonradiogenic -, 33, 37
Lepp, H. and Goldich, S. S., 70, 89, 109, 110, 114, 133
Liebenberg, W. R., 109
Limestone, 78-83, 91, 96
Limonite, 112
London Basin, 22
Lotharingen, 109
Luxembourg, 109
Lyell, Charles, 9, 10, 14-18

MacGregor, A. M., 70, 76-83, 90, 91, 114, 133
Madagaskar, 72
Magnetite, 95, 100, 102
Mammals, 125, 127, 128
Marxist doctrine, 5
Mass spectrograph, 31, 33, 34
Mass spectrometer, 31, 33-37
Mesozoic, 24, 39-41, 132, 133

Metabolism, anoxygenic - (anaerobic -), 59, 60, 82
Metamorphism, 29, 64, 65, 73, 74, 93, 98
Metazoa, 127
Microbes, 47, 67, 70, 75, 76, 92, 106, 125, 131
Miller, S. L., 51, 52
Minnesota, 110
Minette iron ores, 109
Miocene, 40
Mississippian, 40, 132
Missourian, 40
Montmorillonite, 116
Moore, R. S., 131
Morphological diversity of present life, 45, 57, 58, 129
Mountain-building, 64, 65
Muscovite, 116
Mutant, 59

Namurian, 40
Napels, 10, 16-18
Natural selection, 130
Negaunee iron formation, Michigan, 88
Neozoic (= Cenozoic), 24, 39-41
New Red, 112

Ochoan, 40
Oil, 118
Old Red, 112
Oligocene, 40
Ontario, 83-88, 99, 109
Oparin, A. I., 42, 48
Optical activity, 117, 118
Ordovician, 40, 91, 132
Origin of life through natural causes, 2-4, 57, 120, 129
Orogeny, Alpine -, 68

Orogeny, Caledonian -, 68, 73
Orogeny, Grenville -, 41, 113
Orogeny, Hercynian -, 68
Orogeny, orogenetic cycle, 28, 29, 65, 66, 72-74, 112
Oxidation, inorganic -, 46, 49
Oxidation, organic -, 46, 49
Oxide minerals, 95-97, 111
Oxygen, free -, 47-49, 51, 52, 59-63, 92, 95, 115, 118, 120, 134
Ozone, layer of -, 47, 49, 60

Paleozoic, 24, 39-41, 112, 131-133
Parent element, 30
Paris basin, 22
Pasteur, Louis, 117
Pennsylvanian, 40, 132
Permian, 40, 112, 121, 132
Pharusian, 89-92
Phosphate esters, 57, 129
Photosynthesis, inorganic -, 49, 51, 58, 115, 120, 128, 129, 134
Photosynthesis, organic -, 49, 60, 63, 115, 119, 134
Physical clocks, 25, 29
Pirie, N. W., 6, 57, 58, 60, 129
Pitchblende, 31, 99, 100, 104, 106, 109
Placer deposits, 100
Pleistocene, 40
Pleochroitic rings, 26, 27
Pliny the Younger, 9, 14, 15
Pliocene, 40
Polyphyletic origin, 128
Pompei, 15
Porphyrin, 49
Potassium-argon method of dating, 30, 31, 37, 38
Pozzuoli, 17, 18
Pre-Cambrian, 39, 68-73, 77-81, 83, 89-92, 97, 110, 116, 133
Pre-Cambrian, early -, 76

Pre-Cambrian, late -, 75, 91, 92, 112, 121, 134
Pre-Cambrian, middle -, 92, 98
Principle of organic (faunal, floral) evolution, 22-24
Principle of superposition, 22, 24
Protein, 43, 45-47, 57, 63, 115, 121
Proterozoic, 71
Protozoa, 127
Pulse of the earth, 12, 13, 65, 71
Pyrite, 95, 100, 108, 114
Pyrite bacteria, 105, 106, 111
Pyrite sand, 58, 99

Quartz, 58, 83, 94-97, 99-101, 103-107, 111, 115, 117, 118
Quartz diorite, 97, 98
Quaternary, 40

Radiolaria, 75
Ramdohr, P., 6, 70, 88, 98-105, 107-111, 114, 133
Rankama, K., 70, 97, 98, 110, 133
Rapakivi, 41
Red beds, 111-113, 133
Reptiles, 127-129
Rubidium-strontium method of dating, 30, 31, 36-38, 88
Russel, R. D. and Farquar, R. M., 26, 34

Sahara, 89-92
Sand, 96, 97, 99-107, 111
Santonian, 40
Seacow, 125
Seal, 125
Sedimentation, 65, 94-96
Sediments, 22, 24, 25, 28-30, 67, 72, 77, 96-99, 109, 111, 113

Serapis, Temple of -, 17, 18
Serra de Jacobina, 70, 99, 108, 109
Shapley, H., 123
Shield, African -, 72, 76, 77, 89, 90, 98, 99
Shield, Asian -, 71
Shield, Australian -, 72
Shield, Brazilian -, 72, 98, 99
Shield, Canadian -, 71, 77, 83, 98, 99, 112
Shield, Fennoscandian -, 71, 73, 97
Siegerland, West Germany, 110
Silicates, 94, 95, 116
Silification, 76, 83, 85, 87
Silurian, 40, 73, 77, 112, 132
Simpson, G. G., 128
Smith, William, 22
Solar radiation, 122
Spitsbergen, 12
Stabiae, 15
Stromatolites, 90-92
Struggle for life, 19
Sulphide minerals, 95-97, 99, 100, 106, 109, 111
Sulphur bacteria, 111
Svecofennides, 41, 97

Terenin, A. N., 50, 51
Terent'ev, A. P., 117
Tertiary, 40
'Thin soup', 48, 49, 58, 63, 64, 117, 118, 129, 134
Thorium-lead method of dating, 30-33, 37, 38
Tilton, G. R. and Davis, G. L., 69
Time-scale, geological -, 39-41
Torridonian, 112
Triassic, 40, 112, 132
Tsunami, 14
Tundra climate, 95, 96
Tyler, S. A. and Barghoorn, E. S., 70, 77, 83-89, 133

Ultraviolet rays, 47-49, 51, 60

Umbgrove, J. H. F., 12, 13, 65, 69, 71

Uniformitarianism, 7-10, 14, 16-19, 42, 64

Uranium-lead method of dating, 30-38

Varved clays, 21, 25

Vertebrates, 125, 127

Vesuv, 9, 11, 14, 15

Virus, 127

Volcanism, 65, 119

Weathering, 65, 94, 95, 97, 98, 112

Weathering, chemical -, 95, 96

Weathering, physical - (mechanical -), 95, 96

Weathering, reductive -, 98

Whale, 125

Wilson, A. E., 6, 52, 53, 58

Winkler, K. C., 44

Witwaterstand reef, 70, 99-101, 103, 105-107, 109

Young, R. B., 79, 83

Zeuner, F. E., 21